A Candlelight Ecstasy Romance ®

"YOU HAVE TO KEEP REMINDING YOURSELF I'M A COP, DON'T YOU."

"Frankly, I need no reminders," she lied boldly and loudly.

"I thought you liked these little psychological chats. What's the matter, don't I talk as nice as your doctor friend?" he needled her. "You'll have to forgive a poor dumb cop who never learned how to talk properly to a lady. Who thinks that women are only good for—"

"I can well imagine," she interrupted angrily.

"Oh?" Tony smirked. "Believe me, it would be better than you've imagined, Maureen." The use of her first name, so seductively spoken, startled her. "But it's nice to know you've been thinking about me."

A CANDLELIGHT ECSTASY ROMANCE ®

SEDUCTIVE ILLUSION

Joanne Bremer

A CANDLELIGHT ECSTASY ROMANCE ®

Published by
Dell Publishing Co., Inc.
1 Dag Hammarskjold Plaza
New York, New York 10017

Dell ® TM 681510, Dell Publishing Co., Inc.
Candlelight Ecstasy Romance®, 1,203,540, is a registered
trademark of Dell Publishing Co., Inc.,
New York, New York.

ISBN: 0-440-17722-7

Printed in the United States of America
First printing—March 1984

To Our Readers:

We have been delighted with your enthusiastic response to Candlelight Ecstasy Romances®, and we thank you for the interest you have shown in this exciting series.

In the upcoming months we will continue to present the distinctive sensuous love stories you have come to expect only from Ecstasy. We look forward to bringing you many more books from your favorite authors and also the very finest work from new authors of contemporary romantic fiction.

As always, we are striving to present the unique, absorbing love stories that you enjoy most—books that are more than ordinary romance.

Your suggestions and comments are always welcome. Please write to us at the address below.

Sincerely,

The Editors
Candlelight Romances
1 Dag Hammarskjold Plaza
New York, N.Y. 10017

CHAPTER ONE

"Are you having trouble with your knight in shining armor?" Nicki chided her mother as she stepped into the living room. Maureen Ryan was frowning down at her sketches. "Maybe you need to date a few Prince Charmings in order to get some new ideas," she observed while her mother drew.

"In case you haven't noticed, I'm an old lady with a nearly grown-up child. I emphasize *nearly*," Maureen said, studying the sketch before her. She scowled down at the figure on the pad while she considered the advice of her most treasured creation.

"You need some good knight material to date, Mom," Nicki encouraged, then added saucily, "a gorgeous handsome hunk."

"And what, by the way, do you know about dating gorgeous handsome hunks?" she asked her daughter as an afterthought.

"I know other Moms date. Carla's mother dates a lot since her divorce. And Amy's mom dated before she was married again, you know, since her husband died"—Nicki hesitated then forged ahead—"it's just that Father died so long ago. Anyway, all the other mothers are older than you are and they date."

"You and I get along fine. We don't need anyone else. Things will work out and I'll even get a good drawing of Sir What's-His-Face," Maureen added with conviction. "No sweat!" Nicki laughed as her mother nudged her with an elbow.

Nicki stepped to the large bulletin board behind the drawing table. "It looks like you've got all the bad guys done," Nicki said

9

as she took a quick look at sketches of a menagerie of evil-looking creatures. A winged green dragon stared back at her with glinting red eyes.

"I have some sketches framed up of the dragon if you'd like to thumb through them."

"Sure." Nicki's enthusiasm was always appreciated. She was Maureen's best critic and fan.

"Wow!" Nicki breathed, flipping through the sketches with the moving details of bulging eyes, bared teeth, and batlike wings stroking the air in sharp, rapid beats. "These are terrific, Mom."

"Thanks." Maureen Ryan smiled as her daughter continued to flip through the more than 400 sketches of the dragon she had drawn. "These are just part of the scene where the dragon is guarding the villain's castle to keep the brave knight from rescuing the princess." She tapped the stack of now motionless drawings. "These are the ones I've already traced onto cels; the rest are at the studio. I have a lot more to do, but the film as a whole is coming along very well." Maureen was nodding, pleased with the fluid sequence of her artwork, which was a prime concern for any animated cartoon artist.

"Dragons are nice, but," Nicki mused, "I'm more interested in the knight that saves the beautiful princess. He picks her up in his strong arms," she said dreamily, "and carries her off to his castle to have his way with her . . . and they live happily ever after, of course," Nicki relayed.

"Hmmm." Maureen frowned down at Sir Rodney, trying to ignore the underlying tone of sexuality in the childish voice while she tried to picture Sir Rodney sweeping anyone off their feet. He was a series of lines and curves forming a body and face but possessed no inner light; no life of his own. "Actually, fourteen-year-old girls aren't supposed to be interested in such things," she said as she experimented with more lines on the vacant expression on his face. "The hero is supposed to be a role model for the boys."

"Role model!" Nicki chirped. "He needs to be a handsome hunk. These movies aren't just for children, Mother," she complained in that pseudosophisticated tone daughters reserve only for their mothers. "Besides, how many people do you know that really fight dragons and rescue damsels in distress for a living?"

10

"It's a principle of fighting against overwhelming odds for good and—"

"And for love?" Nicki quipped, lacing her fingertips and cradling her chin in them.

"Ummm." Maureen continued to doodle on a sketch of her potential hero, but he just didn't seem like knight material. Sir Rodney had to literally jump off the drawing board and come to life on the screen, but his image remained stiff and lackluster. Dissatisfied, Maureen kept doodling. "You better get some breakfast," she reminded Nicki, turning the subject back to more mundane matters.

"Something quick," she answered brightly, breezing toward the kitchen. "Amy and I are leaving earlier for school today. Amy wants to avoid a group of boys at the bus stop that tease us." Maureen studied the lithe form striding across the formal dining room and into the kitchen. The navy knee socks on Nicki's long slender legs didn't quite meet the hem of her navy wool jumper which was, with a crisp white oxford blouse, the uniform of St. Ursula Academy. As she strided from the room her shoulder-length blond curls bounced and glistened.

Maureen was impressed for a moment by how much alike she and Nicki were at age fourteen and yet how very different. Nicki looked a lot like her mother, pleasant and honest, with the same cool blue eyes. Although Maureen's hair was longer and darker than Nicki's, it was still more blond than brown and always held firmly in a knot or braid. Today she wore it in a long braid that hung down her back reaching nearly to her waist so it didn't interfere with her drawing. Even now, at thirty-four, it didn't seem that long ago that Maureen herself wore the navy jumper of S.U. and hurried off to school in the Chicago chill. Yet Nicki seemed so much more wise and knowledgeable, or was it just more straightforward and honest with herself, than she ever remembered being in early adolescence. In the days of her youth it was a hopeless fate that would befall a young girl who thought of handsome hunks. Now there was no fear.

Nicki had the same fresh-scrubbed, open face, same flyaway hair and engaging smile that Maureen had possessed at that age. Like an innocent country girl, Nicole looked as if she should be on a green hillside tending sheep. Maureen remembered with a

11

cringe what her aunt had always told her: "Maureen, you are such a healthy, wholesome little girl, with roses in your cheeks; you'll make some man a beautiful wife someday." She frowned, thinking that was exactly the impression Nicki would have given her aunt. She would have tried to convince Nicki that marriage was her only future, except Nicole's mother was wiser than to think marriage was a safe harbor for every young girl. The more things change, the more they stay the same.

Certainly the uniform of St. Ursula's hadn't changed; even some of the same sisters that had guided the young women in the old days still taught there. Maureen had bittersweet memories of the school, but she hoped Nicki would be able to continue her schooling there, since it was preferable for many reasons to the local public school. The tuition for the secondary school was substantial and was taking more of a hefty bit out of their budget each month. So they decided to convert a few rooms of their spacious Victorian home into an apartment. Hopefully their advertisement in the *Chicago Tribune* would be answered today or tomorrow. The rent that they asked wasn't much, just enough to cover some of the utilities and the tuition for St. Ursula. Having an astute business sense and a real stake in the funds, it was Nicki who had taken charge of the apartment business. It was so important to keep Nicki in the private school, since it had the academic reputation of being a stepping stone into most any Illinois university. Graduation from the institution nearly guaranteed Nicki the future education she needed.

"I think Myron is really a slavedriver," Nicki called as she released her hold on the swinging door of the kitchen and took several bites of toast. "He's not really your boss; he's more like a taskmaster. You work all the time," she said, coming through the tall wooden arch that marked the entrance of the sitting room, where the drafting table sat.

"Not really." Maureen glanced up at her daughter, frowning at her breakfast. "I've worked with Myron for a long time, Nicki, and he's not only a creative man but a good friend. You know that." She patted the stool next to her chair for Nicki to join her at the table as she had done hundreds of times before when they shared their time. Maureen enjoyed Nicki's company and open-hearted acceptance of whatever came their way. "Things are really humming at the studio these days. It's like a dream come true for all of us."

Maureen had worked for Myron and Sunglow Studios since college, first as a background artist and then as an animator, creating cartoon films mostly for local advertising. But with the help of outside investors, the great break for Sunglow came only two years ago with the release of an animated feature-length film, *The Sword and the Dragon.*

"*The Princess and the Knight* is going to be an even bigger success than *Dragon* was," Maureen enthused. "Everyone at the studio is really excited about it and this type of film has made big strides at the box office too. It means big business."

"You've been working about two years on it now," Nicki said. "Isn't it about done?"

Maureen chuckled. "You must have been too young to remember how long we worked on the other film. It'll take a couple of more years. It may take longer than that if I don't get this character straightened out," Maureen finally admitted. "And I'm up against a deadline."

"You just need some good knight material to talk to," Nicki said smoothly. "You know, research."

"Back in the olden days we didn't think so much about boys," Maureen teased.

"Back in the olden days along with dinosaurs and the Beatles," Nicki teased back.

Maureen enjoyed Nicki's laughter and hoped they would always laugh together. They were friends. "So where is this interesting new philosophy about dating coming from?" Maureen asked, expressively clearing her throat. "*Seventeen* magazine, *Science News,* or letters from Grandma?"

Mary McClure had tried for years to convince her daughter to marry again—for security, for a father for her child, for the sake of marriage—and she was not above stooping to use Nicki for that purpose. But Maureen held firm or ran scared, she wasn't really sure which. She had married for her mother's sake once; once was enough. She would do nearly anything for her mother. Weren't they paying more rent than they could really afford on this old barn of a house for Grandma McClure?

"No place special. I've just been thinking." Nicki answered

13

her mother's question after taking another long drink of milk. "Maybe you're like the princess in your film, maybe you need a knight to rescue you from a spell. I mean you're not really Mrs. Ryan anymore, you could be Miss Ryan or Ms. Ryan—"

"I think you think too much about knights, boys, and handsome hunks." Maureen smiled patiently, touched by her daughter's concern. "Life isn't a fairy tale, Nicki. Life is you and me and a very slim budget, okay?"

"That won't be a problem when we get a call on our apartment," the teenager said brightly as she leaned forward and propped her elbows on the table. To Maureen, her daughter still seemed to be all sharp edges, pointy elbows, knobby knees, and a steel-trap mind, but her woman's figure was ripening too. "I'm glad Grandma McClure let us fix up the apartment. Just the two of us didn't need all this room anyway."

"Grandma needed us to stay in the house to watch it for her while she is nice and toasty in Florida for the winter, so she could hardly refuse our request. Wouldn't it be a dream to get out of Chicago for the winter?" Maureen mused, resting her chin on her hand.

"Mom, I think," Nicki said decisively, still studying the drawing under Maureen's elbow, "I think your knight should be tall, dark, and handsome, instead of this blond guy," Nicki said, reaching over the table to scratch a nail on the drawing. "Dark hair, brown almost black, sparkling eyes, sexy . . ."

"What do you know about sexy?" her mother asked, alarmed.

"Well . . . you know."

Maureen grunted a reply. She was continually amazed at what Nicki did know. She had always maintained that she and Nicki had really grown up together. Maureen had been such an unprepared young mother, still in her teens when she had Nicki. As a result, Nicki was a patient baby who never really learned to be a child. She had been around adults almost exclusively during her toddling years and Maureen had called her a little mother at two and an old lady by the time she reached the ripe old age of five. Apple-cheeked and merry, she was always trying to assure that everyone was tended and cared for. Now she was pulling her own weight in the household. She was growing into an independent, clever, and beautiful young woman.

14

"Honey, would you pick up these things from the market when you get out of school?" Maureen asked, remembering the grocery list and fetching it from the pocket of her full circle skirt and handing it to her daughter—to her friend.

"Sure. Are you going to be working late?" she asked, snatching the slip of paper from her fingers.

"I may be if Sir Rodney doesn't pep himself up," she said with a smile that faded into thought as she looked down at the sterile sketch.

"Be careful on your way to and from school. Don't be late; sometimes you and Amy chat too long," Maureen said as she watched Nicki carry the dishes from breakfast back to the kitchen. "And wash the milk moustache off. . . ."

"Oh, Mother!" Nicki fumed as she pounded through the swinging door.

Maureen smiled. She'd been saying the same thing every school day for ten years, and her daughter always had the same disgusted reply.

"And who are these boys that are teasing you and Amy?" she asked.

"Just boys." The evasive answer was muffled in the distance.

"Boys from St. John?" Maureen asked as her daughter swung back through the door and scooped up her books from the dining room table. Then Nicki trudged on to the halltree in the entry.

"I don't know," she said as she shrugged into her powder blue ski jacket that she pulled from a wrought iron hook on the carved frame of the halltree.

"Nicole? Do they wear the St. John uniform?"

"I'll get the groceries." She rushed her words as she edged toward the door. " 'Bye, Mom!" Her voice trailed away as she slipped out the front door. "Have a good day." The door closed and Nicki scurried down the walk that crossed the broad lawn, patches of green grass still showing between masses of late-fallen yellow oak leaves. She hunched down into her jacket, hiding from the November wind that whipped at her legs. She was nearly to the street by the time Maureen reached the etched door glass.

Maureen watched Nicki from the window before she was swallowed up by the stately oaks and maples that lined the street of her childhood home. Maureen could hardly look out over the lawn in the fall without remembering her older brothers tossing a football or gang-tackling one another into sweating heaps. It always seemed that her young life revolved around an oblong leather ball spiraling through the air, up for grabs.

Maureen's father was a small-construction contractor who built many of the houses in the suburbs of the city and established a very comfortable home for the McClure family right here on Clover Street, in the Austin community. But his pride in life was basking in the glory of his athletic sons. Maureen was the youngest of the clan and the only girl on the McClure team. She spent most of her young years convinced that she was adopted because she was, first of all, a girl, because she lacked the thoughtful green eyes of the rest of the family, and because her name didn't begin with the letter *E*. Since her parents had started a pattern with the boys of following the alphabet, she thought surely they found her in a glen guarded by the leprechauns. Alf, Brian, Chuck, and Derry—A, B, C, D . . . E? Maureen was the misfit E. She was quiet, intense, and intellectual in contrast to her burly, mule-headed, hard-nosed brothers, who played football first at St. John and then at Notre Dame, where they monopolized so many Saturday afternoons, running and dodging.

She could remember individual plays being rehearsed and relived on the dining room table, using the salt and pepper shakers, creamer, and tumblers as the front line, and a spoon as the back or wide receiver, the frosted globed chandelier glowing softly over their heads. Mother's dining room was always a pale green—as it was now—that blended with the oak wainscoting and open stairway that came down into the elegant room, an unlikely setting for a steady, unadulterated diet of the rock 'em—sock 'em of football.

The McClure brothers were revered and worshiped for their prowess on the field and Maureen's parents were active and prominent in the city's political and social circles. Respected and popular, they were always asked to sit near the mayor's table at important political functions. Who would have ever guessed that pretty, bookish, unassuming Maureen would ever cause her family so much embarrassment? Not even Maureen, in her most vivid dreams, could have foreseen the events that would lead them to such shame. For an instant Maureen thought about the handsome public school boys at the bus stop so many years ago and how she ignored them as instructed by her parents and wondered if Nicki ignored them now.

Maybe today would be the day for their ship to come in on the advertisement in the *Trib*. Maybe . . .

She glanced at her watch, turning to her drafting table, stuffing some sketches into her portfolio, and grabbing her coat. Even if the apartment rent came through, she still needed her salary from the studio and she would be late for work if she didn't hurry. She and her knight in shining armor were facing something even more fierce than a fire-breathing dragon—a deadline.

CHAPTER TWO

It was early afternoon and the shadows didn't reach beyond the sidewalks on Twenty-Eighth Street in the Near South Side. Despite the chill in the air, there were old men propped in doorways and gathered on the corners. Captain Tony DiRocco stepped from the Twenty-Eighth Street Police Station and got into his departmental car waiting out in front. He eased the car away from the curb and threaded the gold Dodge through the narrow streets through traffic and past abandoned cars. He sped by the iron-barred and boarded-up storefronts and bleak highrises as a white tornado of old editions of *The Defender,* Baby Ruth wrappers, and past campaign posters whirled in the streets behind the bumper, floating to a new, unnoticed resting spot. He would soon be having a pleasant lunch with his sister downtown, a world away from the police station, the pressures of his office, and from the rubble and litter of the Near South Side.

Indian summer was past, fading away from memory along with the forgotten campaign promises, while frigid breezes blew off the lake, dropping the crime rate nearly as quickly as it dropped the temperature. The winds of November made his police work just a little less hectic and the residents of his district safer. It kept the fair-weather purse snatchers and muggers off the street, cooled the domestic quarrels that had steamed in July, and dampened smoldering tempers. He was thankful he had survived his first summer as captain of the eruptive Near South

18

Side and was very grateful that the temperatures had lowered. It was only a few blocks from his district to the Loop, but the difference was like night and day. The city with the "big shoulders" was glittering and thrusting up from the foot of Lake Michigan, but the ghetto surrounding the Twenty-Eighth Street Station House was somber. The highrises facing the street stared down at him with bleak bare windows, old despite their youth.

The neglect and apathy in the Near South Side was criminal, but it never made the blotter or came across his desk at the station, where Tony captained a work force of 300 of the Second City's finest. The weather was a balm that cooled a sizzling crime rate and gave Tony a little more breathing room, at least until the holiday chaos.

Once on State Street it was only a few minutes to the Loop. He cruised along, gazing at the crystalline skyline of Chicago visible above the steel girders and platform of the elevated train that ran along the street. The smoky Sears Tower jutted up among the other smaller skyscrapers into the crisp blue sky. To serve and protect—it seemed more possible with the security of the concrete and glass obelisks hovering above him and the sun dancing on the blue water of the lake. He always had a feeling of being akin to the city; it was part of him; it was him with its bold crisp lines reaching up into the sky. But he had a love affair with the lake—vibrant crystal blue water always giving beauty and pleasure to the city, thrusting up at its pliant shore.

The el roared overhead as the staunch fortress of the Chicago Police Headquarters came into view. It was a forbidding four-story structure of brick and glass, a less than subtle reminder that police power was a real and political force in the Windy City. Tony was considered by some of the rank and file to be grooming for the royal guard of that castle, since he moved up the ladder so fast. But, knowing full well how politics drove the city, Tony couldn't stomach politics. His superiors knew he was an ethical, independent bastard, his own man, one that could get the job done and would not become a political threat. That's the reason he moved up so fast.

After a short drive on Washington, past the iron and steel Daley Center, and a quick squealing turn, he pulled his car into a parking garage and walked to Sergio's, a favorite restaurant of his sister, Linda. He would meet her there, just a few blocks from the county building where she worked as the assistant district attorney. When he was told she hadn't arrived yet, Tony agreed to take a table to wait for his sister and he ordered their drinks. Tony smoothed his dark brown hair and waited impatiently, nursing a Collins as he sat in the luxury of Sergio's. Waiters in red jackets bustled between the tables and ornate chandeliers glowed above the white-linen-covered tables.

He took another long taste of his drink. That was another thing he added to his mental list. He usually didn't order mixed drinks, but lately everything was going crazy. Everything was changing, yet everything stayed painfully the same. He felt restless, itching to be on the move, but he seemed to remain either standing still or he moved in slow motion. Hadn't he developed a sixth sense while on the job on the streets? He knew what was going down. He was getting stale—maybe because of this desk job.

Hadn't his reputation in the department been built on his quickness and efficiency as well as his grim determination not to let anyone get away with it—any crime, any injustice? His fast thinking, catlike ability to always land on his feet, and his speed were the qualities that his brother officers and his superiors alike respected. It was voiced in the roll call that Tony DiRocco could outthink and outrun any skell on the streets of Chicago. He couldn't be bought or outrun. If DiRocco was after you, you did your time. He always got the collar. The story that clinched his legendary reputation was the one about how Tony ran down an armed felon in a getaway car fleeing from a bank robbery while he himself was on foot. He was always smart, always fast, and always exercising that sixth sense. He kept his body in shape since he was a rookie. He jogged and worked out on a heavy bag to clear his head. Lately it seemed the harder he punched the bag the better he felt. He was as clean as a choirboy—no politics, no bribes, and he wasn't killing himself with booze. He was on top of his career. Then why did he feel so sluggish? He was forty years old, damn it, that was the trouble. He knew it all along. The lack of juice wasn't about his career; it was something else. And his sixth sense was telling him that no amount of work or recognition on the force would cure it. He took another long swallow of his drink.

He saw his sister greet the maître d', who made a fuss over her. Little wonder, she was an independently wealthy woman in the political heart of the city and she looked radiant in a camel-colored tailored suit and a soft shiny blouse the color of liquid copper. Her dark hair, cut short and stylish, complemented her high cheekbones, full lips, and large brown eyes. She looked beautiful, confident, and in control. Tony could never remember when she didn't give that aura, even as a child. He stood as the maître d' guided Linda Scarpelli to his table.

"Happy birthday, little brother." Linda greeted her brother with a kiss on his cheek as he helped her with her chair. "Well, do you feel a year older?" Linda asked, smiling, settling down for a pleasant visit.

"I feel ancient," he confessed. "I have scars and creaking bones to prove it."

"You look terrific to me," she judged with a sister's teasing voice. "It still aggravates me that you inherited all the naturally thin genes. And just remember, you can't get old or I will too."

"Not you," he assured her. "I ordered some wine for you."

"Thank you, Captain DiRocco, supercop," she teased him broadly. "With your desk job it looks as though you may even survive your war against crime. I can't believe it'll be your first anniversary at the Twenty-Eighth soon. To a good street cop and now a good captain." Linda saluted him with her glass.

Tony nodded. "Papa always said I was good at beating on windmills," Tony laughed, allowing a momentary wave of nostalgia to wash over him. He would be glad when all this birthday business was over. "He told me I didn't even look like a cop, remember? 'Who ever heard of a cop in this city that wasn't Irish and big as a bull,' he'd say." Tony remembered.

"He complained and gave you a rough time. But he was very proud of you, Antonio." She watched her brother finish his drink, which prompted a waiter to hustle to the table with another round and take their orders. After he glided away from the table, Linda asked brightly, "So what are you going to be doing with all your spare time since you've settled into your new job?"

"This desk jockey is going to find himself out on the curb if

I don't find a new apartment soon. I received notice last week to buy my apartment as a condo or vacate."

"Why don't you buy? You may want to settle down someday —"

"You know how I feel about that . . ." He really didn't need to finish his sentence, since he'd said it so often before.

"I know you didn't want to leave a wife and family behind if anything happened to you while you were working on the streets. But you have a nice safe desk job now, Tony. So . . ."

"So, is there anything your office can do about these condo companies?" he asked, ignoring her question.

"We've always got cases on that hot potato," she answered, then fell silent as the waiter brought Tony another drink and left again. "Thanksgiving is coming up and we want you to spend it with us. Will you be inviting anyone special to come along? You know, your dates are always welcome," Linda said, trying not to be too heavy-handed as she shifted the topic back to one of her choice.

"No one special," he said nonchalantly, hoping to can the whole subject, but he knew that was impossible.

"Why not?" she asked incredulously. "You no longer have an excuse for not getting involved. You can't be afraid?"

"Hey, hey, what's this afraid business? Don't you know you are talking to a bonafide hero here? I'm not afraid of anything." Tony teased his sister in a confident tone, but he could feel his sixth sense jumping in a jittery beat.

"Yes, I know you, masked crusader. You're not afraid to walk on any street in this city," she said. "I grant you that. You don't ever fear for yourself even when you should. But loving people . . . ?" Linda shook her head. "You've used your badge as an excuse for years. That shield does come off at night, little brother. It's not tattooed to your body and soul."

"It's not that complicated, really. I'm not seeing anyone because I'm feeling particularly ancient right now," Tony chuckled self-consciously and tugged on the vest of his smart three-piece suit, and glided an impatient hand over his hair. His sister's determined stare was continuing evidence she wasn't going to let him off the hook that easily. "I just can't go up to a woman and say, how would you like to go out with an old broken-down cop.

22

It's just not a real effective opening line, if you know what I mean? Besides, I meet a lot of lovely empty-headed women, and before I know it they're asking me what sign I am, if I like to disco, and your place or mine? I don't know." He felt ridiculous trying to explain to his sister changes that he didn't understand himself. He had appreciated generous empty-headed women for years, but lately nothing was the same.

"Perhaps you're ready for a more meaningful relationship," she said smoothly.

"Meaning more permanent?" he asked. But she only cocked her head, pursed her lips, and gave him a knowing look. "Let's just forget about my love life for now, all right?" His sister agreed, shrugging gracefully. There was an uncomfortable silence between them until Tony's tone rose. "By the way, how's your sex life these days, counselor?" he asked flippantly with a devilish grin before he tipped his glass, allowing the whiskey to warm his throat.

"Tony!" she shushed him.

"How's Gerald and the kids?" He rephrased his question, smiling as his sister glanced about the restaurant to see whose ears had perked up at his remark.

"Busy, growing . . ." she said, starting to recover. Tony chuckled. He still enjoyed making his sister blush. He could remember so many times when they were still at home and her boyfriends would come over. He had always felt it his duty to make sure the young men were worthy of his sister's attention. He had weeded them all out except for Gerald, a wealthy businessman, who worked for a large construction company that engineered projects all over the world. But he had even given Gerald a rough time. He was doing it again, remembering back, recalling old times, ancient feelings, and the neighborhood. He had been reminiscing for weeks; no wonder he felt so old. But at least he could still make Linda blush. He wasn't that far over the hill. Linda was the one person he could count on to help him, make him laugh, and zap him between the eyes with the truth. He nodded his head, listening to her tales of the latest escapades of his niece and nephew and of Gerald's upcoming trip to the Middle East while they ate their lunch in the leisurely atmosphere of Sergio's.

"Thank you," Tony said at last. "For the lunch, I mean. The

men at the stationhouse sang 'Happy Birthday' to me this morning, but somehow an off-key group of desk sergeants, street cops, and detectives just doesn't make it. Thank God I don't turn forty every day." Linda laughed at Tony's expression.

"Oh, Tony. Your life is just beginning, if you would only let it," she advised him. "Allow people to reach you. Don't be afraid to love, Antonio. Isn't that what you tried to tell Papa?" It was nice to have a sister to remember birthdays, but it was cruel that she also remembered his own words and turned them against him. But Linda he could forgive.

Tony pulled his gold watch from its little pocket in his vest, released the latch, and the case popped open. After checking the time, he snapped the delicately engraved case closed, thinking about how many times he had observed his father check the same timepiece with the same deliberate calm, to give himself just a little reflecting space or shift the momentum of an argument. He slipped the watch back into his pocket, wondering if his father had been afraid to love and lose again after his wife had died.

"I'm due in court soon, counselor," he said, giving his sister a wink. "Thank you, Mrs. D.A."

Sinking back into the seat of his unmarked police car, Tony drove across town. After testifying in court and checking back with his office, he was free to follow a few leads on a new apartment. He had surveyed the ads in the *Trib* and after a lot of reading found a half dozen apartments that fit his paycheck and his life-style. He called to make an appointment with a manager in the suburb of Maywood. He snatched up the paper to reread the address of the circled ad before dropping the paper onto the seat beside him. He was valiantly trying to rid his thoughts of condos, birthdays, and memories, concentrating on the fringes of static and the incessant monotone of the police dispatcher who kept him tuned in to the city.

He hated the idea of moving, getting used to new people and a new landlord. Those objections were ludicrous. He had always paid his rent by mail and he could count on the fingers of one hand the times he'd seen any of the people that lived in his apartment building. As an unmarried detective, he didn't have what was considered regular hours. Long and hard, yes, but often not in step with the rest of the world. It had been only since his last promotion that he was keeping a pace even close to the nine-to-five crowd, except if there was an emergency in his district. Linda was right. It was time to allow himself to know people other than cops and robbers. But did he have to start his new life in the suburbs? It was too far from his work, not convenient like his apartment in "the gap," just a few blocks from his station house.

He drove on, approaching his old neighborhood. He had grown up on the edges of Austin in a comfortable house just a few blocks away from an old established Irish neighborhood. Chicago was a patchwork of small neighborhoods with deep roots and pride—where Italy and Ireland could lie only blocks apart. His father was a creative and successful lawyer who had moved his family from Taylor Street to the pleasant community of Austin. He was near his old high school and close to a flood of old memories when the dispatcher broke into his thoughts. There was a call for any unit near the O'Neal Market on Bonner Street. There was a purse-snatching in progress at the familiar corner grocery store, and Tony was only a few blocks away. After an instant of internal arguing, he turned on the siren and radioed the dispatcher, placing a flashing light on the roof of his car. How many other units could be so close? No problem, just get the guy, request a back-up, and wait for a radio car to show. It couldn't take more than fifteen minutes. But Tony DiRocco was an off-duty officer on his way to a new life. He would do as his sister suggested; he would take off the badge—maybe tomorrow.

As the Dodge flashed by the parked cars, he could see a group of young boys surrounding a small teenage girl, pushing her from one to the other, taunting her until one reached out and grabbed the bag of groceries she held clutched to her chest, ripping the brown bag and starting an avalanche of apples and meat tumbling onto the sidewalk.

The Dodge came squealing to the curb; boys scattered in all directions, ducking into doorways and sprinting for the alley. Tony flung the door open and charged after them. The young girl called after him, "Please, no, it was nothing." He rounded into the alley and saw two of the fleeing boys about midway up the

25

dusky cavern. He walked a few more paces, his hand hovering above his gun and holster, but something told him the two boys collapsed and panting against the wall were just that—school-boys pulling pranks. For a moment he could envision himself and his old childhood friends folded over in laughter after some ornery stunt.

"It's the police," Tony shouted, putting the thunder of God in his voice. The sallow-faced boys did a Looney Tune double-take before tripping over one another and scrambling out of the alley. He watched them for a while before going back to the present and leaving the alley.

He walked back to the girl, her blond hair spilling over the shoulders of her powder blue ski jacket. She was intently gathering the scattered food from the concrete, her small handbag and some books lying near her feet. She seemed all right. She silently picked up the spilled groceries, since the only thing that remained in the nearly useless bag was a half gallon of milk.

"Are you all right, miss?" Tony asked, lifting her up to her feet. Large blue eyes stared up at him, reflecting open admiration and gratitude, but still she had no reply. "Are you all right?" he repeated with a small smile, unaccustomed to such unabashed scrutiny.

"Yes, thank you," she said at last, her cheeks staining darker. "Are you really a policeman?" she asked, befuddled. "You don't look like . . ." She was fumbling for words, but her wide eyes never wandered from his face. "I mean—thank you for helping me."

"What's your name, miss?" Tony tried to get to the business at hand. He wasn't in the girl-rescuing business; he was an off-duty police officer going to see about an apartment on his way to a new life. And now he had a kid on his hands and maybe a report to file.

"I'm Nicki. Nicole Ryan." He noticed she was wearing the navy jumper and blue socks of the St. Ursula Academy, but the dismissal bell had rung hours ago; the sun was nearly setting.

"Nicki, it's really too late for you to be out on the street alone," Tony reminded her, wondering why her parents would allow her out. "Do your parents . . ."

"My mother was working late, but she should be home by

26

now." Tony watched her face, remembering walking blocks out of his way to see the S.U. girls at the bus stop. But they never gave him the time of day because he went to public school. He had the grades, but during his high school years his family didn't have the money for St. John. So each morning he jogged a few blocks to catch a glimpse of the perpetual source of sweet perfume, and smiles. It was always an exercise in frustration because the girls wouldn't speak to him or the other public school boys, so they would tease them. Traditionally the women of St. Ursula were to seek no further than the men of St. John's. He was beginning to have a clearer picture of what might have been happening just a few minutes earlier.

"I'll call a unit to take you home," he said.

"No, please. It's all right, officer," she said earnestly.

"I'm Captain DiRocco of the Twenty-Eighth Street Station," he said gently. "Did you know the boys, and do you want to make a complaint?"

"Yes—no." She started quickly, then paused. "They're boys that I see at the bus stop every morning," she explained needlessly. "They usually don't bother me. I really don't want to make a complaint, is that all right?" He nodded, amazed at her compassion as she smiled at him, showing a raft of metal braces. He had forgotten how really young teenagers were. The ones that came into the station house were old and hardened beyond their years. "I mean Danny wasn't with them today. I think that's why they got so—" she volunteered.

"So you think some other boy put them up to this?" Tony pressed.

"Oh, no! He would never do that. He's really very nice." Tony glanced up quickly from his notes. His sixth sense told him that some lucky kid named Danny had a cute little Irish girl soft on him. Maybe Tony wouldn't need to call and wait for a radio unit.

"I don't know why . . . they tease us," she said, bewildered.

"Probably because they like you and want your attention," Tony said absently, weighing other questions. What to do with one teenage girl when it's too late for her to be walking home alone? Unfortunately now it meant more of a delay, either taking her home or waiting with her until a radio car could come for her.

"Do you really think so? Do you think that's why they tease us?" she asked as though it were a novel idea and had never occurred to her at the bus stop over the years.

"Yes." He couldn't help being shocked by her lack of ego. "I think if the boys tease you, it's because they like you and want to get to know you better."

"But why don't they just talk to us?" Nicki asked after considering his words carefully.

"I don't know," Tony said, remembering he'd never considered such a direct approach as a kid. "Maybe it's because they don't think they have a chance with you anyway. Don't the St. Ursula girls still date the boys from St. John?"

"Only the girls with air heads and big bosooms," she nodded sarcastically.

"Now, is that any way for a young lady to talk?" Tony asked, stifling a laugh.

"What about Danny, does he go to St. John?"

"No. He's very nice," she qualified. "Very smart too. He takes geometry and chemistry. He's usually with this group of boys, but he won't speak to me and—I don't know— Do you think he may . . . I don't know?"

"So you think Danny is an okay kid?" Tony said, watching the blue eyes light up.

"Yes, really! He's very smart and quiet."

"Just walk straight up to Danny, introduce yourself, and ask him to walk you home, and I promise you won't have any more trouble with the others and you'll be safer too," Tony assured her, then cautioned Nicki protectively. "But only allow him to walk you home." Tony frowned, remembering what usually happened when he had walked a beauty home.

"Yes, sir." She smiled at him with disarming openness and he felt his professional demeanor deteriorating. He felt like a guarding brother again, but he knew he was old enough to be this kid's father. "Thank you."

"If you don't mind, I'll take you home now," he said, gathering up more bruised apples and putting them into the torn bag. All these polite "Yes, sirs" were aging him fast. "Did we get all of your groceries?" She nodded as he guided her toward the car and opened the door for her. Nicki put the food items into the car and gathered up the newspaper that lay there before she settled herself in the seat.

"I've never ridden in a police car or been rescued before," she said in childlike excitement. Tony nodded. Everything was relative. How many times as a kid had he dreamed of rescuing a girl and protecting her from all the harm in the world? But now it merely meant a delay. "You really don't fit the picture I have of a policeman—" He snapped the door shut and walked around the front fenders of the car and slid behind the steering wheel. This was hardly his picture of police work either, but he was going to become a person now, not just a cop, right? "Captain DiRocco, were you a policeman in the olden days?"

"Olden days?" he groaned as he pulled out into traffic. "Yeah, I was a cop back when Teflon coated only frying pans not bullets. But that was sometime after Jesse James." Nicki laughed and watched him speculatively as he reported on the police band that the eight five one call on Bonner was a false alarm. She listened vaguely as she studied the newspaper that she had gathered from the seat.

"Were you a policeman before dinosaurs and the Beatles?" Her eyes were so clear and innocent as she anticipated his reply that he couldn't take offense.

"Before, I think," Tony admitted with a smile.

"Are you looking for an apartment, Captain DiRocco?" She asked with peaked interest, noting the circled ads. "I'd be glad to help you find one. It's the least I could do to repay you."

"Helping young ladies in distress is just part of my job," he said gallantly but without a smile. He couldn't believe she seemed to take him seriously. She nodded reflectively as she studied his profile.

"Just turn left at the next corner," she said, directing him to her home. "Here's a good one," she said enthusiastically, pointing to an insignificant ad squeezed in among the myriad of condo pitches. "It could be just what you're looking for. A small apartment in a nice neighborhood."

"I don't think . . ."

"Nice landlord, beautiful house, warm, friendly atmosphere— turn right at the next corner," she directed him. He shot a puzzled glance at the young girl. "And how often would you get

29

an opportunity to help put a teenager through school? The rent would just cover the tuition."

"Tuition?" Tony asked, watching the street ahead. "Is this apartment at your house by any chance?" Nicki was sitting on the edge of the seat now, winding up for an earnest sales pitch.

"It's a very nice apartment," she nodded. "It's furnished. And I promise I won't play my radio too loud. The rent's cheap too. How often would you get a chance to live next to a real artist and a precocious teenager?"

"I'm looking for a bigger place," he said flatly. But he already knew this resilient kid better than he knew anyone at the apartment building where he had lived the last seven years. How much change could he muster in one day?

"Of course, if you need more space for a wife and family . . . Do you have a family? Or a wife?" she asked weakly, bracing for the answer.

"No, but I—"

"Please, Captain, say you'll at least look at the apartment. Please." Tony looked away from the pleading face, wondering whether he always had to be a cop, twenty-four hours a day. He restored what little demeanor hadn't been eroded by the winsome teen and preserved it with a mask of professionalism. "I'll just take you home, Miss Ryan, and talk to your parents." Her expressive sigh was decidedly one of disappointment, but she quietly leaned back against the seat, watching a few stubborn leaves tumbling from the oaks and maples that lined the street.

"My house is the large gold one with the black shutters in the next block. The apartment is on the first floor." She angled her head in its direction. Seeing the seeds were sown on stony ground, she sighed again more deeply. "You can pull into the drive."

"This isn't a social call, so I'll just pull up at the curb," he said, disliking the coldness in his tone. It was distracting to discover that he was still a sucker for St. Ursula girls after all these years. He drove past the house, made a screeching U-turn in the middle of the street, and parked at the curb in front of the gracious Victorian home, wondering why it was necessary for someone who owned a house like this to rent rooms in order to pay for school tuition. Her parents must have real problems. Hadn't she

30

said her father was an artist? He shut off the engine and popped out of the car, avoiding the pleading sky-blue eyes. He reached the passenger side and opened the door, but Nicki remained stationary.

"Please, at least say you'll look at the apartment," she tried again, looking up at him.

"Nicki. Let's go talk to your mother," he said, plugging up the leaks in his professional armor. How could an irresponsible adult have such a sweet kid?

"I'm really not a bad kid," she said. "I promise I'd stay out of your way. You wouldn't even know I'm around. Please say you'll look at it."

"Okay! Okay! I'll look at the apartment. Just look," he cautioned her, pointing a finger at her. "Understand?" His tone held all the toughness he could muster.

"Nicki!" He heard the voice behind him.

"Hi, Mom." Nicki called proudly with a grin. He turned from the girl to face a new danger—the form of a Nicki Ryan grown into a beautiful, graceful woman. Her face glowed with wide-eyed innocence, only a slight frown weighing down the corners of her pouting pink childlike mouth, but her sensual body belied that illusion. She wore a rose sweater that hugged the curves of her high, firm breasts with enticing softness, and a matching full plaid skirt that swayed with sensuous ease around her hips and thighs. Her light honey-blond hair—he couldn't decide the color —was long and hung in a single braid past the center of her back. Stray beams of the setting sun caught it, changing the color from amber with highlights of apricot to the shadowed tones of a silver fox. Her hair was swept back from her nature-girl face, a face that any soap manufacturer would crave to claim responsibility for.

All his practiced warnings and speeches about the dangers of the city streets left his head. At last he found something great about being forty years old; it made a gorgeous mother of a teenager look very young and very sexy. He parried distracting visions of starting his new life and his only coherent thought was an image of her unrestricted hair draped like spun gold over her shoulders. She was obviously a woman of quality and he knew instinctively that she wouldn't care if his sign was Scorpio and

31

wouldn't try to convert him to vegetarianism. She was a beauty with a native intelligence that gleamed from her vibrant blue eyes instead of the vacant stare he'd too often encountered in other women.

He wanted to invite her to fly with him to Rio or Rome for the weekend, but she looked more like the type who would rather go for a walk in Lincoln Park—with her husband—some damn lucky Irishman. As she approached he reminded himself he was no longer a schoolboy at the bus stop, but a professional who knew his job. He surrounded himself with the invisible protective armor of a seasoned cop.

CHAPTER THREE

Maureen had nearly convinced herself to call the police, when the shiny gold car pulled up to the front of the McClure family home. Seeing Nicki safe sitting in the front seat of the vehicle, she released the breath she held for what seemed like hours. She rushed from her vigil at the window to the door and broke from the stifling grip of dread into the crisp air.

"Nicki," she sighed, watching her daughter smile but not recognizing the driver of the car. The man in a tan coat and navy suit got out of the car, briskly rounding its front fenders as his unbuttoned trench coat swung open with each stride. His conservatively cut thick black hair was touched with gray and framed a dark, handsome face. His sharp features and warm brown eyes were set in a serious earnest expression. Maureen tried to picture him as the father of one of Nicki's friends or an official of the school, but he didn't look like a teacher or a school administrator. She didn't have time to speculate as Nicki hopped out of the car.

"Nicki?" Maureen called out to the girl braced against the car as she quickly took the front steps in a flurry and strided along the walk.

"Mom."

The man turned to face her with a melting smile that startled her for an instant. His mouth curved infectiously, showing white teeth and crinkling the short lines fanning from his eyes. But the attractive grooves in his lean cheeks disappeared as his smile faded while he studied her. All of the animation left his face and his stance tensed. His long coat disguised many details of his physique, but it couldn't hide the energy radiating from his well-proportioned frame.

"Nicki, what happened?" Maureen asked, but her voice was airy and not as forceful as she wanted it. She looked toward Nicki, trying to avoid his dark, unnerving gaze that never wavered. He was observing her so closely that she felt as though she were being scored on her every move, every feature. Yet, from his stoic expression she couldn't tell whether she was passing the test.

"This is my mother, Maureen Ryan," Nicki said, barely glimpsing the tip of her mother's distress. "It's okay, Mom. He's a policeman."

"Mrs. Ryan." The officer acknowledged her with professional courtesy. She nodded silently to the introduction. He appeared an unlikely candidate for the police department of the Windy City, being of medium height with broad shoulders and chest, but lacking the typical gorilla quality of every other cop in Chicago.

"What happened?" Maureen asked again.

"I stayed too late at Amy's, then I remembered the groceries." Nicki rushed the words. "I went to the store and—"

"I'll explain to your mother, Nicki. Why don't you take the food inside." He interrupted Nicki in a voice that brought to Maureen's mind the sultry sound of a tenor sax. It was the first time he spoke in more than curt monosyllables and she was surprised by his pleasant, mellow voice, but she couldn't be fooled by it. She knew there was an iron-hard cop facing her. He gently moved the girl toward the car as he sliced a glance at Maureen that demanded her agreement. There was action behind his alert eyes, wheels turning, intelligence gleaming from their brown, almost black depths. They made her nervous. These eyes knew things, could see a lifetime in a glance, and could lead her into a trap if she wasn't careful.

"Mom?"

"Yes." She nodded. "Take the groceries into the house, honey," Maureen said to her daughter, who was reluctant to

34

leave. "This won't take long." Why was he studying her so closely? She watched Nicki gather the apples, a head of lettuce, and some potatoes, stuffing them into the remains of the tattered paper bag, clutching the plastic wrap of a loaf of bread, and hurrying toward the house. Maureen used the opportunity to study the officer as he watched Nicki. Up close his face was even more interesting and attractive than she had first thought. His deep brown eyes held a look of compassion and intelligence, but his expression remained unyieldingly serious. He gave Maureen the heady illusion that she could look him square in the eye although his shoulders were several inches above hers, despite her high-heeled boots. She guessed him to be an inch or two shy of six feet.

"We should go inside also, since you're without a coat," he suggested. She was listening to the tone of his voice again, and not to his words.

"No . . . that . . . no. I would rather you explain why you brought my daughter home," she insisted. Maureen compulsively used her left hand to smooth back the wispy stray hairs at her temples in a nervous response and held her wedding ring up as an amulet to turn back the powerful force of his encompassing regard. Did she see his shining eyes soften for an instant?

"I responded to a call on Bonner Street. Your daughter was just leaving the O'Neal Market and—" He paused. His quick gaze didn't miss a detail. His eyes scanned the house and grounds, gathering information and formulating impressions, she could see, his scrutiny undermining her confidence. ". . . There were a group of teenagers near the store . . ." For an instant the officer allowed his perusal to go beyond professional interest as his gaze slipped from her face to linger a second on the curves of her breasts and hips. His penetrating regard sapped her fire nearly as quickly as the occasional gusts of wind flowing through her thin sweater. ". . . And I chased them away. Your daughter shouldn't have been out alone."

"Are you insinuating that I'm not a responsible parent?"

She folded her arms over her bosom, unsure of whether she was stemming the cold or thwarting his upsetting observations. "I don't understand."

"You understand that it's your responsibility to know where

35

your daughter is," he said. His frown furrowed two short vertical grooves between his dark brows, pointing to a line that crossed his forehead.

"I—I got home from work . . ." she stammered angrily as she remembering the sinking feeling of walking into an unexpectedly empty house. "I know my duties as a parent, Officer." Her temper was rising along with her voice. "I thought I did know where—"

"You shouldn't send her out so late. It's not safe for a young girl to be walking on the streets alone, even close to sundown," he ground out, controlling a temper that was unfurling slowly like a ball of string. She dreaded seeing its full strength. Speaking with obvious restraint, he added, "Any parent should know better than to allow their daughter—"

"Allow?" she shouted. "Do you think I didn't instruct her to come straight home after school? Allow! How many children do you have? Are you really a police officer? You don't even look like a cop!" At last she struck the blows that ruffled the tough exterior of the cop, and that pleased her.

"I assure you, Mrs. Ryan," he said stiffly, "I am a police officer." Brushing a hand past the lapels of his coat and jacket, he pulled an ID from his inside pocket, flipping it open for her inspection in one smooth, long-practiced movement. She stared at the gold badge glinting like a burnished shield in the setting sun, thinking he was too young to be a captain. Captains certainly didn't look like him when she was young, yet the ID and picture verified his words.

"Captain, it's not your job to tell parents how to raise their children."

"I know my job; it's just that some parents don't know theirs. Where's Nicki's father? Maybe if I talked to—"

"I think you've said quite enough already. Too much! I'm going to report your conduct to your supervisor, Mr. DiRocco," she said, hating the empty threat.

"It's Captain DiRocco," he corrected her, his straight white teeth clamping together, working the muscles along his jaw. "Don't forget to note the badge number, ma'am," he added with unwilted fortitude, holding the shield up once again before flapping it closed with a bold snap and replacing it in his pocket.

"They'll be hearing from me." She gave her final shot and whirled about, intending to leave him obliterated on the sidewalk. Undaunted, he took a half step and caught her arm and held her firmly in a grip she knew could be painful if she resisted. His smoldering gaze held her wide blue eyes and confirmed her guess that it was useless to struggle. His touch on her arm loosened, but Maureen was trembling inside.

"Lady, I don't know what you do for a living, but I'm a police officer," he said. Dark fires of emotion leaped from his eyes. She could feel her heart thudding against her ribs as his closeness stampeded her thoughts and reasons for her hostility. "I'm very good at my job, Mrs. Ryan," he drawled. "Regardless of your opinion, I don't spend my day beating in heads, harassing small children, or using thumbscrews to make old ladies talk." His eyes glinted with a smoldering fire as he searched her upturned face. "I just responded to a routine call that turned out to be schoolboys playing pranks. Nicki's fine. No need to thank me, of course. I just hope there's someone around when she's really in trouble." He breathed out trapped air and emotion. "Do you know what I mean?" His voice softened as he watched her face blanch. She knew very well what he meant. How many times had she suppressed that horrifying feeling when she had been waiting, worrying and telephoning friends. "I see too many victims in my work, Mrs. Ryan. I just don't want Nicki to be one of them." His quiet tone along with tiny, almost inaudible, catches in his voice distracted her and eased his harsh words.

Maureen was speechless, staring into the infinite depths of his soft dark eyes, marveling at how quickly they had changed. In their depths she could see a warm inner light, possibly compassion, certainly pride. He held her gaze forever before he abruptly released her arm and took a safer, more appropriate step away. He was apparently shaken by his speech, but he covered it well by slipping a hand inside his jacket to his vest and pulling out his gold pocket watch, checking the time. He noted her recovery as she memorized his every move. He snapped the watch shut, never taking his gaze from her, replacing the gold piece with what seemed like a ritual of premeditated calm. "I really should be going," he announced. "I'm glad I could bring Nicki home safe."

37

"Captain DiRocco, please, don't go! You promised!" Nicki called from the porch, closing the distance between them quickly. "Mother, Captain DiRocco rescued me today, did he tell you about it? He's really terrific! He's also looking for a new apartment, and I told him about ours and he promised to look at it," she reminded him, grinning. "Please, you promised you would look at the apartment, just look," she begged, "even though there's none better in the city. Where else could you have such charming and lovely landladies? How can you resist?" Mother and daughter stared at the officer, Nicki with pleading round eyes that openly worshiped her new hero and Maureen's wide blue pools reflecting astonished confusion. He turned a wonderful smile on Nicki that crinkled the lines at his eyes and deepened the creases on his cheeks.

"I'm sorry, kid. I don't think it's a very good idea. Although I have to agree about the landladies," he said, smiling, as he took one last look at Maureen Ryan. "But I do hope you find someone." His smile was warming her despite the chill. "Good evening, Mrs. Ryan," he said casually, as if their entire conversation had been enchanting.

"Good evening, Captain," she answered, matching his nonchalance, as though his smile had no effect on her erratic heartbeat and as though his sparkling brown eyes didn't melt something deep within her.

He spoke to Nicki as Maureen feuded with herself. She should have insisted that he look at the apartment, but she was reacting so rashly to this man. The giddy motion in her stomach was an undeniable trouble signal. Those kinds of problems she could live without very well. Hadn't she done so for years? Why allow one handsome man to shake her? A cop no less. He would be gone in a few minutes, rolling away in his unmarked car. She had made a terrible mistake by acting so defensively and she should apologize to him. But she refused to compound the error by asking him to see the apartment. Just thank the man for bringing Nicki home safe and he'll be gone forever, she coached herself.

"Thank you—for bringing Nicki home," she said, swallowing a large lump of pride along with her doubts. "I'm sure she'll fill me in on the heroic details." He nodded, tugging on one of Nicki's curls.

"It's just part of my job," he directed at Maureen. He cruised Maureen and her daughter with his radar. "Police work is a lot easier, though, when we get cooperation from people in the community who care." He took one last sweeping portrait. "Mrs. Ryan." He nodded, slipping his hands into his coat pockets and backing away.

"She's really *Miss* Ryan!" Nicki said, stopping his retreat.

"Nicki!" Maureen shot a scolding look at her daughter while trying to freeze the heat rising to stain her cheeks.

"Ma'am," he said as a smile crinkled the corners of his eyes but refrained from turning his mouth. "Miss?" he corrected himself, allowing his gaze to drop to her staunchly crossed arms and back to her eyes. If he was surprised, it didn't reflect in his features or in his voice. She guessed the totally controlled man to be about her age, certainly old enough to know better than to be so unsettling.

"Being a single parent isn't always a predictable business," she started her explanation. "Some days, miscalculations are made and any assistance is greatly appreciated." She gave him a brief smile and he accepted it.

"You promised to look at the apartment," Nicki whispered.

"Honey, we've detained Captain DiRocco long enough," Maureen said, twisting her shoulders to block the view of his laughing brown eyes and to ignore the apparent pleasure he got from her renewed embarrassment. "And you know we really intended to rent the apartment to a woman," she said, unable to censor the words as they tumbled unrehearsed from her lips. Her sentence stopped Tony DiRocco in his tracks. He did an about-face with a calculating expression on his face, once again putting Maureen distinctly on the defensive.

"Is that your official renting policy, Ms. Ryan?" he questioned her, narrowing his gaze. "No men allowed?"

"I really—"

"Do you know it's against the law to discriminate in housing for race, creed, or sex, even when it's only chauvinistic males you're trying to keep out. I would hate to go back to the station-house empty-handed," he baited with a slight smile. "And the D.A. is always interested in these cases."

"I . . . I . . ."

"It would be a shame to have to run you in for a fair housing violation though." He shook his head empathetically. "It's really a nasty court procedure, long and costly. Perhaps I should see the apartment," he said dramatically and with more than a hint of a threat. "That would get you off the hook."

He walked past her without another word or a backward glance while an exuberant Nicki joined him, excitedly breaking into her sales pitch like a pro, including the pleasant neighborhood and archaically reasonable rent. Maureen stood motionless as she watched the companionable pair walk up the front steps. It wasn't really like Nicki to pay undue attention to men, yet this police captain was a rare breed, she had to admit. Her thoughts tumbled in a baffling tide, but they couldn't give relief to the floundering feeling of panic. Why was she so damn disturbed? Antonio DiRocco was a cop all right, a very clever one, she dared not forget that. But he also had endeared himself to her level-headed daughter, besides churning up a wake of energy and emotion whenever he looked at the mother.

Just moments ago she was sure that she would never see Tony DiRocco again, but now he was walking confidently up the front steps of her home. And she realized that the old stuffy Victorian was nearly begging for the vitality he exuded. Before he stepped over the threshold he looked back at her as a smile tugged at his lips but never quite reached its full power. It was strange, Maureen mused, how quickly and deeply she'd been affected by this man. He was indisputably handsome, vital, and dangerous. He moved well, with athletic grace, without the overpowering thick-headed brawn that Maureen had vowed to avoid after growing up with four muscled giants like her brothers.

"Come on, Mom," Nicki shouted happily while Tony DiRocco gave Maureen the patient and guiding gaze of a righteous priest before flashing her a devilish grin and disappearing into the house like the Cheshire cat.

The sight of a man's coat hanging on the ornate antique halltree was startling in itself, but a sensual male voice drifting from hidden rooms of the house was completely unsettling. Maureen glanced into the mirror of the halltree and a survivor looked back. She could hear Nicki expertly explaining details of the apartment and Tony DiRocco's deeper, interested tones rumbling after hers. A masculine voice sounded foreign in their home, as she and Nicki had been together, just the two of them, for so long with only the ghost of Kevin Ryan to disrupt the duo. It was strange to think of Kevin now. She had nearly blocked the memory of her deceased husband from her mind. Maureen stood tenuously in the archway, not knowing whether to back away or enter the morning room, one of the four rooms reserved for the apartment. It was a small, dark sitting room with a carved oak mantel over the fireplace and glowing wainscoting. It was a toasty room on the east side of the house, where her mother had resolutely completed correspondence and her parish commit-teework early in the morning as the sun splintered in through the one stained glass window.

Nicki guided the captain through the apartment, leading him from the morning room to a small bedroom, bath, and the entrance of the dwelling, in a small efficiency kitchen, at the rear of the house. As he retraced his steps and entered the morning room, his trim body looked tall next to Nicki's lithe frame, although the daughter was only a couple of inches shorter than the mother. His smart pinstripe suit couldn't hide the fitness of his torso that tapered down to a trim waist and narrow hips. His striped tie was knotted precisely at the snug collar of his white shirt and the cuffs showing fashionably below his jacket sleeves made him look more like a financial dynamo from LaSalle Street than a cop. Why was he a cop? It seemed so unlikely. Why did it feel stifling in this room?

"He likes it, Mother." Nicki smiled. An additional heat wave tumbled over her as she fell under his sweeping appraisal.

"I'm sure Captain DiRocco was looking for something a little larger and—"

"You mean something more family-size?" he finished her sentence with a playful tone. "You were right before. The Waltons I'm not. No ties, Ms. Ryan." He was studying her with a measuring expression on his face.

"I see." She still wavered in the archway, undecided as to whether it was safe to walk in. His disturbing regard and a tiny draft of air in the archway kept her from the swallowing vacuum of his attraction.

41

"I'll go get the papers." Nicki chortled as she whisked past her mother into the dining room and up the open stairway.

"Nicki, I think we should give the captain time to think about . . ." Maureen's voice trailed off as she watched her daughter climb the stair with determination. She turned with an apologetic sigh to face the police captain, who was watching her expectantly. "This is a very quiet neighborhood . . . I really feel you would . . . I know there have to be more exciting places in the city to live," she stammered on, his dark questioning eyes following her every gesture and inflection. It was entirely too warm in the house. The sweater that let the cool winds pass through while outdoors now held her own body heat to her warm skin.

"I would like a quiet place," he nodded truthfully. He walked around the sofa and coffee table as though he were on a grand tour of a museum, deceivingly interested in features of the room, but his gaze strayed only fleetingly from her. His tour took him beyond the sofa to the fireplace and started him back to the archway where she stood. For a moment he was framed by the colored window, his sad eyes and long straight nose and high cheekbones giving him a particularly innocent quality.

"But a teenager around—that always causes confusion . . . you know . . . music, telephone calls, giggles. Girls—you know." She was unsure she would be able to discourage him from taking the apartment, although she was most certain that she needed to, despite the boyish amusement sparkling in his eyes.

"Yes, I know something about girls," he said seriously. The darker shadow of his jaw and chin and the message of impatient sexuality flowing from his movements and from his eyes backed up his statement. He was no choirboy, but a man. She looked away quickly when she felt him reading her thoughts.

"Then you know how hectic it would be," Maureen rushed on blindly. "Loud music, pajama parties . . ." Maureen's voice faded as a tiny illusion of a smile turned up the corners of his mouth.

"Pajama parties?" he asked, intrigued. "Sounds very interesting." The innuendo in his words caused her to blush along with his encompassing regard and her own straying thoughts. She retreated a step, bumping into the wooden arch of the door, and stayed there for the support and security of the sturdy oak. His

42

enjoyment of her embarrassment was insufferable along with the heat of the room.

"Mr. DiRocco—" she started firmly.

"Since we're going to be neighbors, you could call me Antonio or Tony." He smiled, closing the distance between them.

"Neighbors?" she gasped incredulously. "Captain, I don't think you understand. . . ."

"Now, let me see if I've got this straight," he said, placing a hand on the doorpost near her hip. He was so close to her she could scarcely get any air. It was as though he were breathing her share. "This door," he said, his dark eyes laughing despite his serious demeanor, "will separate the apartment from the house?" His magnetic eyes were holding her and the moist, reedy tones of his voice drew her closer, like the notes of the Pied Piper.

"That's right," she said, alarmed, breaking their spell and slipping away from him to pull the sliding door from its hiding place in the wooden frame. She rolled the door to the center of the arch as the captain slid its mate from the opposite frame. The two high oak doors kissed in the center with a solid knock. "It would be locked, of course," she assured him as she demonstrated the lock with a reassuring click.

"Of course." His voice was low and directly behind her. She spun around with her back to the door and stared up into his handsome face, realizing too late that she had locked herself into a vacuum with the man. His dark brown eyes searched her troubled blue ones as her heart pounded mercilessly against her ribs. "These doors would be the only thing to separate us?" He leaned closer still, gazing at her lower lip, which she moistened quickly with an involuntary flick of her tongue. "I would be on this side of the door and you and Nicki would be on the other?"

"Yes." The word was barely above a whisper. Her voice as well as her thoughts were beyond her control. This was ridiculous, impossible. An intelligent, resourceful woman who had survived and fended for herself and her child for fourteen years was shaking in her high-fashion boots. Trembling, because a man with mesmerizing eyes and a voice that made common questions sound unbearably exciting was challenging her long-held policy of isolation. *Enough already! Enough. You're a woman, not a scared rabbit. Throw this Mediterranean flatfoot out on his gold badge*. He would be nothing but trouble and the butterflies in her stomach proved it. Maureen Ryan was much too old and much too smart to fall for that trap no matter how tender. She turned defensively and fumbled with the lock.

"I suppose the door locks from both sides?" His question was teasing and unnervingly suggestive. She slid the doors open quickly and darted through the narrow space, giving herself more breathing and fighting room. It was all she could do to keep from running into the comparative safety of the dining room.

"I think you had best leave now," Maureen declared in what she hoped was a commanding voice. She spun to face him to emphasize her words.

He was propped casually against the doorframe, his arms folded across his chest and his head tipped to one side. Following her every move, his mocking eyes were perusing and reading her with aggravating ease. She edged around the end of the large walnut table in hope of scrambling his messages. She gained courage with more distance and a table between them.

"Thank you for bringing Nicki home and for taking the time to look at the apartment, but you should leave now before she comes back down." She motioned toward the large oak stair. "I'll explain the situation to her."

"No one could accuse you of high pressure sales tactics, Ms. Ryan," he chided her, lifting a dark, taunting brow. "Being a cop has made me a very suspicious man, kind of an occupational hazard." He apologized off-handedly as he left the archway and moved into the dining room with her. "Generally," he started to say, sliding a hand into the pocket of his slacks and rumpling up one corner of his jacket, "when a person tries to brush off an officer they have something to hide or are afraid of something." He moved steadily around the table toward her. "Are you afraid of something, Ms. Ryan? Or do you have something to hide?"

"We're asking a lot of money for the apartment. I know on a policeman's wages it would be nearly impossible," she said, backing away from him, admitting at least to herself that he was a very large threat to her peace of mind. She was nearly at the foot of the stair that faced the golden light of the entry hall.

"You don't need to worry about the rent. I'm good for it." He stroked a hand over his jaw, evidently considering what she did and didn't say, with some sort of cop-deciphering code. "And besides, I've always wanted to be a scholarship fund for a St. Ursula student," he added.

"You and Nicki certainly had a full discussion on the drive back." She coughed, placing a hand on the carved newel post.

"Yes, we did," he said in deceptively simple words. "Your daughter is a very open and caring individual." His eyes hinted at the more complicated story of her mother.

"She's very young and impressionable, Captain. I'm sure she sees you as a hero today," Maureen started to say dryly, planning to slip in the ego-bursting "but." "She's really a child in that way; she seems to need heroes." Maureen avoided the eyes that dissected her words.

"Nicki's a good kid," he said at last. "I'm glad she needs heroes. It means she still has dreams."

"Maybe she dreams too much," Maureen said, lifting her chin and meeting his gaze head-on, remembering another young girl who dreamed too much.

"Here it is!" Nicki called cheerily, descending the stair into the quiet room with a ledger and receipt book in hand. "I hope you two got better acquainted." She smiled.

"Whose name do I write on the check?" he asked, noting Maureen's tight expression. Maureen and Nicki started to talk at once, but Nicki's voice was heard, since that was the positive voice he was listening for.

"Mine," Nicki said proudly. "I'm the business manager. Mom's the artist."

"Temperamental, I presume?" he teased her, glancing through the large archway near the base of the stair at the drawing table crowding the other furnishings in the formal sitting room. "You'll have to do well in school now," he qualified, looking at Nicki.

"I will," she promised with a metallic grin. "And I'll follow your advice on the way to school tomorrow. Thank you very much, Captain DiRocco."

"Call me Tony. Okay?"

"Okay," she agreed. "Do you really think what you suggested will stop the boys from teasing me at the bus stop?"

"Guaranteed." He gave her a brilliant smile. Nicki's uncondi-

45

tional approval was sealed when she surprised him with a kiss on his cheek. Maureen was amazed at the stony captain's sudden shyness at the genuine sign of affection. "Maybe I should get into the girl-rescuing business more often," he said, a new timid smile forming. It was not as confident but extremely appealing, and Maureen felt a tug deep in her middle. "Well, let's make the apartment business official," he said decisively, camouflaging his feelings as he opened his jacket to pull out his checkbook and pen. Maureen was about to protest, until her attention was drawn to the tan leather holster under his jacket that was strapped snugly to his body and fit under his left arm. The dark wood and metal butt of his gun was slung forward for easy access. When his jacket closed again there was only a slight bulge that she hadn't noticed before.

"Thank you, Tony," Nicki said as she took the check from his long fingers. "Here's your receipt and the keys to your apartment." The check and receipt were traded. It was official. Tony nodded after her, then looked in puzzlement at Maureen's pale face. "We're all set then," he said, opening his jacket to replace his checkbook and pen. He noted curiously her apparent gaze locked onto his gun. "I'll be back in a few days." She looked up into his face, the dark eyes filled with questions and concern.

"You're wearing a gun," she whispered in a hushed tone.

"I always wear a gun when I work," he said, seeing the stiffness in her body. "Every cop in the city does."

"Mom's afraid of guns," Nicki squeezed in, "she's strictly a nonviolence person. She was even arrested in the big antiwar demonstration in town. I was just a baby but . . ."

"Nicole!"

"Arrested?" He swung his attention back to the infuriated young woman.

"This is my home. You can't stay here with a gun," she said, her anger flaming along with the color of her cheeks.

"This is your home. That" he said, pointing into the morning room, "is my apartment!" He irritatedly shrugged his shoulders, then breathed out purposefully. "Believe me, I'm a trained professional. I'm not a cowboy riding into town on Saturday night to get drunk and shoot up the town, okay? I'm one of the white hats, remember?"

46

"No guns."

"I protect little ladies like you."

"Yeah, Mom, how many jobs do you know that includes saving damsels in distress?"

"Nicole, please! Captain DiRocco was just leaving," she said. "We will remit your rent."

"Mother!"

But he remained infuriatingly still except for his hands flexing at his sides. It was a standoff of wills; neither could back down. "Nicole, would you please go upstairs? I'd like to speak to the captain alone."

"I'll see you in a few days," he said, nodding agreement to the teenager. She took the stairs painfully slowly. Maureen watched his bold profile for an instant as he watched his new friend climb the stair. Traitorously, Maureen wished she and this dark-eyed stranger had met long ago, possibly in another era, and for a millisecond she explored the fascinating possibilities. But she reined in her imagination harshly as he turned to face her.

"I can't . . . I refuse to have a gun in the house with my child," she said, emotion splashing in confusing tides in her mind.

"I'm not a child." Nicki's voice piped her objections from the landing at the top of the stairs.

"Nicki, please go to your room!" Maureen called out, sounding like a mother. How long had it been since she'd had to make such a command? "Will you please leave, or do I need to call the police?" she asked Tony DiRocco in a steady voice, not conscious of what she was saying.

"I *am* the police, lady!" he flamed in exasperation. "I have rented your apartment and I will be moving in soon."

"I refuse to rent to a person who carries a gun." The pitch of her voice rose with the tension in her body. "Guns are . . . they are dangerous around children. Contrary to your opinion, I am a conscientious parent and I'm not at all sure whether I'd like a policeman living in my house," she huffed.

"I would like to change your mind about that," he said with maddening patience and a gaze that didn't miss a detail of her face. "I know this may come as a surprise to you, but this badge isn't tattooed to me. It does come off at night, and so does the gun. You may discover having a cop around the house isn't so

47

bad." She fathomed in that moment that she could discover a lot from this man, too much, she decided as she looked away from his insistent gaze and lashed out at him.

"But . . . but you work with criminals all the time."

"It's not catching."

"What if some crazed person followed you here—"

"Oh, yeah. I see what you mean." He nodded and spoke confidentially from the side of his mouth. "If some crook hears on the street that I'm puttin' the squeeze on him, he won't like that, right?"

"Right," she agreed, helplessly mesmerized.

"He might even come to rub me out some night while I'm sleeping. Is that what you mean?"

"Something like that," she agreed, fascinated by the tension and excitement of his scenario, sketched out almost like a movie. The smile in his eye told her she had walked into his trap, and he was teasing her.

"Believe me, the best thing for you to do is stick close to me." His statement was as intensely sincere as his gaze. "I've been a cop for nearly fifteen years and haven't found a crook at the foot of my bed yet."

She'd been had by his quick mind and winning charm, but she couldn't answer. She turned dramatically and walked to the entry hall at the bottom of the stair, feeling like an actress in his play. She wanted to laugh at him and herself, but she knew that wouldn't fit the part and she'd be lost to him forever.

"I'll get your coat." Her voice was tiny splinters of ice falling into a warm pool. Was she being melted down one small crystal at a time?

"Don't bother," he said brusquely, following her lead. "There's just a few more things I'd like to get straight," he said, catching her arm and turning her around to face him.

"And what is that, another joke?" she asked, forcing an edge of frost into her voice. "I fail to see the humor or purpose in guns or violence, Captain DiRocco."

"There are a lot of perpetrators that use guns. That's why police have them. There's a war going on out there in the streets, Ms. Ryan. And someone has to fight it, to serve and protect lovely innocent ladies like you. I'd really like to try your philosophy of make love not war sometime," he said pointedly. "Maybe you could explain it to me." Before she could object, he went on. "But as it is, there are bad guys who would blow a person away for pocket change. And this isn't Hollywood, lady. They don't come looking for us, and the victims don't live again in the next movie." His lean hard body moved toward hers.

"What kind of cop are you?" she retorted. "Are you trigger happy, on the take?" The question was intended to blow his cool self-assurance out of the water, but he never flinched.

"I'm very good," he stated with painstaking honesty. His expression was serious and his features were sharp except for his saintly, sad eyes. But his body was tense and poised, like a cat ready to spring to the attack. A tiny smile almost reached his lips, when Maureen was startled by brushing against his coat and nearly bumping into the halltree. She could retreat no farther.

His eyes narrowed and a muscle worked along his chiseled jaw as he caught his breath before forcing out each word. "I always get who, or what, I'm after," he said, his voice scratching out the words on stone as he moved closer. "Always," he pledged solemnly to round, unblinking seas of blue and a pair of shapely pink lips forming a silent O. His gaze scanned every feature until he concentrated on the soft, parted lips that started to speak, but his intensity held her silent. She began to shake her head, but long fingers caught her chin and a thumb brushed along her cheek as he held her firmly. "Always," he repeated, his voice a sultry saxophone crooning blues in the golden twilight filtering through the etched glass of the entry hall.

She tried to speak. She wanted to come back with a withering retort, but he hovered above her, confident and engaging. Lord, was she falling into a dream again?

"Tomorrow I'll send a man over to install a telephone. I hope you'll cooperate with him. The police department needs cooperation from people of the community."

"No, you don't understand."

"I'll be looking forward to my move," he said as he surveyed her softly curved body not made any harder or less enticing by her blazing temper. "It's a very nice apartment," he qualified. He slowly took his coat from the halltree and with purposeful calm laid it over his arm.

49

"You can't move into my . . . house," she shouted. *Nor into my life,* she vowed.

He opened the door and stepped out, facing her for one last, encompassing look at his devastating victory.

"Good night, Ms. Ryan," he managed to say with infuriating innocence before Maureen cried out with an outraged gasp and slammed the large front door, rattling its antique brass knocker almost as much as his charm had shaken her carefully cloistered passions.

CHAPTER FOUR

The twisted, uneven smile in the pasty face mocked her as her pen glided over the sketch and added lines to the form, struggling to find the right look for Sir Rodney. With each ink stroke the blond knight only taunted her, his expression seeming to say, He really got to you, didn't he? You were foolish enough to let a tough guy with ice water in his veins pull your strings. He must still be laughing at her. How could she have melted like that? A cop!

She had tried to keep the captain out of her thoughts, but even the lifeless ink drawing of Sir Rodney brought him to mind. Unbidden images of Tony DiRocco wearing a chain mail hauberk and polished armor filtered gloriously into her mind like the golden light reflected from the Holy Grail. These daydreams only paled the knight of her sketches, making him look even more feeble and bland. She slammed her pen down on the table. Hadn't she seen this one before? What happened to the intelligent Maureen, the resourceful, down-to-earth practitioner who knew the answers, how to follow her rules, and how to play the game? Maureen had argued for several days and finally had herself convinced that it had been only her fatigue and worry about Nicki that had made her so vulnerable to the needling cop that evening. She had slept very little that night, disturbed by the vibrant memories of Antonio DiRocco, but eventually she purged him from her mind that night and through her busy days.

Just when she was sure there were no residual effects from their first encounter and when she considered herself cured of the temporary insanity he had caused, he called.

"Hello," she had answered brightly yesterday, expecting Myron to be calling about sketches. "Hello?"

"Good morning, Ms. Ryan," Tony DiRocco said. "You sound beautiful in the morning." The phone couldn't disguise his voice. Just hearing its sultry quality cascaded an avalanche of doubts and emotions over her again. She heard the husky notes that made it unique, entirely Tony DiRocco, supercop. Finally he spoke again to her stunned silence. "This is—"

"Yes, Captain," she said shortly, forcing a tone of morning frost into her voice to cover the weakening feeling in her knees. "I know who you are." But she didn't recognize the woman who clung to the phone, steadying herself against the newel post of the stair. Unpredictable sexual vibrations were buzzing through her body at the speed of light. There was an uncomfortable silence as she listened to his breathing.

"I need more of your cooperation . . ." He hesitated again. There was, gratefully, no way he could hear the red flush creeping up her neck. Damn him! She couldn't speak and she started to quietly replace the receiver. "Don't hang up!" he commanded. Inexplicably she returned the instrument to her ear.

"What do you want, Captain DiRocco?" It was infuriating that he could read her thoughts over miles of telephone cable. She knew she would never be safe from this man. The man who had shattered her carefully obeyed rule—no men—was moving in. She had allowed someone to move into her life once before. It had had tragic consequences. She had married a boy once; once was enough. So she had become a champion at keeping men from making a pass. She wrote the book on thwarting the old "wine her–dine her–bed her" routine. She had learned the hard way, but she wasn't going to give up now. It had been easy to keep other men at a distance or as friends since her first marriage, but this man . . . The old arsenal of techniques had little effect. But for both their sakes, she would find a way to keep him at a safe distance.

"Your cooperation is greatly appreciated." She could hear a smile in his tone, but she had no idea what he had requested. Yet instinctively she predicted that he would someday ask her for what she was unable to give. "This may be my only chance to get you into my bedroom," he said lightly, but he left a poignant pause.

"What?" she breathed, her heart thudding. She knew it wasn't him she needed to fight, but her own attraction for the man. He thought she was a dizzy little broad. Wasn't that what tough guys thought about women? Especially blondes. Damn. He was definitely not her type. *I don't have a type,* she strictly censured herself. *No men, period, end of conversation.* She was forming a devastating retort that would bring this conversation quickly to an end.

"Just answer when it rings, okay?" He left no room for debate before he hung up the phone.

"Okay," she answered feebly, listening to the silence on the dead line and swallowing her unsaid caustic, witty remark. She became angrier as she envisioned how many other women fell for the handsome cop. The picture of a stable full of brunettes and redheads at the beck and call of the Italian Stallion infuriated her even more.

In the distance the phone rang.

"Captain DiRocco, you won't be getting any cooperation from this little filly," she vowed scathingly into the receiver that she still clutched in her hand.

The phone rang again. She looked stupidly at the silent phone in her hand. But the strident ring still beckoned from the new phone in the apartment. A few seconds later she sat reticently on the bed Captain DiRocco would soon use, listening to his enticing mellow voice along with all the alarms ringing in her head. The test of the newly installed phone lasted only a few minutes, but it managed to set her mind whirling for the entire day.

"I'll be moving my things in tomorrow. Saturday," he added, seemingly reluctant to finish their conversation. "Maybe I'll see you then," he said. It really wasn't a statement or a question, but had the gravity of a black hole that Maureen was sure would swallow her up just as she had been drawn to the depths of his dark eyes.

"Maybe," she agreed. "I'll be working tomorrow," she added as a safety net.

Working! That statement was laughable, she mocked herself, dragging her thoughts into the present, back to her sketches and script that lay neglected on the table before her. She read the line of film dialogue over again. She tapped her pen on the drawings and looked through the archway, across the dining room, and into the apartment as she had done for the one-hundredth time this morning. She had read the same line from the script a dozen times, but she was distracted by the activity in the other rooms. This was moving day for the new tenant.

> Sir Rodney: "Fair Princess." (Sir Rodney salutes as he speaks, then bows his head.) 32 frames. At this time the audience must know that the knight loves the princess.

It took at least thirty-two sketches to get all those actions and to produce the mouth movements for that bit of dialogue. Plus in those thirty-two pictures it must be evident by expressions and twinkling eyes that Sir Rodney loves Princess Margo. They were probably the most crucial frames in the first half of the film, and Maureen was stymied, remembering other beguiling moments and sexy velvet eyes. Maureen pondered how she could capture their dark intensity and emotion on film. That was ridiculous. A rigid police captain wouldn't translate onto the screen any more fluently than her knight. Yet Sir Rodney was still an inanimate, unfeeling mass of lines greatly lacking the charisma of the tightly wrapped, hard-boiled cop.

As though her thoughts conjured him up, her new tenant appeared in the morning room. He shed his all-weather jacket and pushed up the sleeves of his camel-colored rugby-style sweater as he teased Nicki. He was relaxed and joked with his moving crew as his athletic body was framed by the oak archway. The large doors were not yet closed or locked. He was wearing brown slacks that fit his narrow hips snugly, suggesting the shape of strong thighs below the fabric. His casual sweater-vest with several buttons undone fit his wide shoulders and tapered to his trim waist. The light color of his shirt compliment-ed his dark features and the hint of gold in his high angular cheeks. It was difficult to keep her mind on her work when she was thinking only about him. It was impossible watching him. She put down her pen and walked to the archway to close the door of the living room. He turned to assess the movement he caught from the corner of his eye.

His appreciative regard fell on her like sunshine through a window, and she couldn't help but smile.

"Good morning," she said, easing his encompassing gaze that took in every detail of her fuchsia sweater, blue jeans, and the roses staining her cheeks.

"I was right," he said earnestly, "you are beautiful in the morning." His sad brown eyes swept a pattern over her and finished their survey at her pink lips as he stepped to the archway. Nicki rushed to fill the embarrassed silence as she followed him.

"We've got everything moved in," she said happily. "Now all we need to do is unpack, right?" she asked Tony.

"Right." Tony smiled at the teenager.

"Wow! You've really got a great smile. Doesn't he, Mom?" She requested verification.

"Yes, very nice," Maureen concurred, studying it objectively, although she could feel more heat on her face.

"Absolutely fantastic!" she praised Tony airily. "Who did your dental work?" Nicki asked, unable to contain her line of thought.

"God," he answered seriously, being careful not to smile.

"Gerry Rosenbloom does mine," she chattered on, shaking her head. "He's my orthodontist," she explained to Tony's puzzled look. She smiled, showing Gerry's handiwork. "He's a good friend of Mom's."

"A good friend?" he asked, swinging his question to Maureen.

"Yes. A very good friend," she answered coolly, seeing the wheels turning in his head. She could tell by his expression that he thought Gerry Rosenbloom must be a romantic interest. She saw no purpose in explaining that Gerry was the husband of a friend, another studio artist.

"Would you like me to start unpacking some boxes?" Nicki offered Tony, shooting a suspicious glance at her mother.

"Sure. There's some boxes of books in the main room. That would be a good place to start." Tony smiled.

"Wow!" She muttered to herself as she turned to find the books. Tony remained, watching Maureen. They peered across the dining room at each other, she wary, and he devouring her, but neither moved.

"I—I've been working," she finally got out, gesturing toward her drafting table. Everything she said sounded so stilted. *He must think you're a dumb blonde.*

"I've been moving in." He almost smiled, tipping his head slightly to look curiously at her long hair. "Do you always wear your hair like that?" He studied the intricate braid that formed a silvery rope nearly to her waist. "It's very long. I like it."

"I really should get back to work," she said quickly, disallowing his compliment and shying away into the living room.

"I would like to talk to you. It'll take only a minute," he said, stepping into the pale green no-man's-land of the dining room. "I'm unarmed," he said, assuring her by raising his hands and turning a small circle. The dark hair of his sturdy forearms and the curling hair just above the V of his shirt distracted her. "I packed my gun away." Then why did she feel more threatened than ever before?

"Away?" Her numb tongue was apparently only capable of babbling in monosyllables. Her eyes were involuntarily drawn to the tantalizing dark mat that formed a small triangle above his shirt, but she forced herself to look away as he came closer. He knew. His handsome face creased into the beginnings of a timid smile that caused her heart to skip a beat. There was no doubt he knew how disturbing he was to her.

"I know the gun bothers you." His voice was a ballad singing a sad tale. "So I won't wear it around you."

"Thank you." She couldn't look at him, so she concentrated on the weave in the carpet. He continued to close the gap between them. "I know it's difficult," she started, focusing on his chin and jaw, but soon her gaze dropped lower, "for someone like you to understand how I feel when you're so . . . so . . . hmmm."

"So?" He obviously wanted to hear her impression.

She shook her head. She could hardly admit to being attracted to a man, a dangerous, vital man who carried a gun.

"I don't want you afraid of me." He lifted her chin with his fingers. "Okay?" Her pulse was scurrying through her veins as she returned his searching gaze. His jaw was darkened with a shadow of a beard and she wanted to touch its rough texture and ached to trace the gentle outer curve of his lower lip with her finger. His potent masculinity disturbed her, warned her.

"But you would still wear a gun to work," she said, moving deeper into the living room. She couldn't allow his attraction to let her forget he was a cop, a comrade-in-arms to the riot police that had arrested her years ago. She really didn't feel strong enough, however, to attack, so she retreated away from him.

"Yes," he said flatly. "I'm still a cop."

"Yes, you are," she agreed, thinking he was also a very dangerous man that was blowing any semblance of order in her mind. She would be glad when he was confined to his apartment out of her sight. And out of her mind, she hoped futilely. "I really should get back to work now," she said. She felt uncomfortable standing with him in the center of the room. His body was tense, like a tightly wound coil, and she couldn't be sure what he was going to do next. Seeking refuge, she moved to her drawing board, which afforded a safe barrier between them. "I'm glad we had this little talk," she said, picking up her pen as though that little gesture would dismiss the powerful man from the room. But he stood unbanished, as dark and vital as ever. He held her with a dark gaze as a cautious thumb brushed along his hard lower jaw that jutted to the side. She could sense his radar vibrating through her. What was he finding? What information were her averting eyes giving him? The answers he received were apparently satisfactory. He sauntered casually toward the table, an impatient hand rattling coins and keys in the pocket of his slacks. Keys to the apartment, no doubt. How was her resolve going to survive with him living next to her? Her regard flicked over him, unwilled but totally invited by the male magnet that drew her deep feminine desires to the surface. She wondered how many women would use the extra key to his apartment.

"I'm really quite busy, Captain DiRocco." Her words were much sharper than she had intended. What message did he

57

receive? He was reading what she did and didn't say with aggravating skill.

"Yes, I can see that. Don't let me bother you," he said, nonchalantly strolling to the storyboard behind her. "Just go on with your work." He gave her a small crooked smile, but it wasn't real. She loved his smile, but this was more of a warning.

"Ummm." She scraped her teeth over her lower lip and turned her back on him and touched her pen to the paper. Pretending he wasn't there was like Tweetie Bird pretending not to see Puddy Cat. Her heartbeat increased as he moved closer to her, and he was ignoring her magnificently. She knew that because she stole sidelong glances at him. He studied the sketches of creatures on the storyboard as Maureen stippled ink on the sketch of the waning Sir Rodney.

"Do you always draw such frightening creatures?" he asked, his natural curiosity apparently taking over after studying the dragon.

"It's an occupational hazard," she said dryly, pushing her wheeled chair back so she could see the drawings and Tony DiRocco's expression. "Captain, I really don't understand you. You know I would have rather had a . . . another tenant and still you insist on staying here," she said, pursing her lips. "Do you always stay where you're not wanted?" She tipped back in her chair, smiling smugly.

"Are these drawings for a book or what?" he asked, unflapped, blunting the sting of her cheap shot. He seemed intrigued by the detail, and deaf to her question.

"I draw for a movie studio. These characters will be in a feature-length film."

"A movie?" He spoke softly. "So this is the stuff dreams are made of and you create them here." He looked at her as if the clouds had rolled away, and then back at the pictures. "But this guy," he said, pointing to the dragon who stood on his hind legs, "looks more like a nightmare. Did you draw him?"

"Yes. All of these are my characters."

"You are really good," he said innocently.

"Thank you." She nearly smiled at his enthusiasm.

"Who slays the dragon?" The intensity of his question caught her off-guard.

58

"The brave knight of course—"

". . . who in turn gets the pretty girl at the end of the story, right?"

"The princess," she corrected him.

"Of course." He swept her with an appraising regard that she swore she wouldn't react to. He almost smiled, as the lines around his eyes creased and a knowing sparkle reflected from the brown eyes. "Who is this guy?" he asked, pointing to one of several sketches of Sir Rodney on the table. She swung her chair forward to face the table.

"That's Sir Rodney, the brave knight, the true love of Princess Margo." She enlightened him with a lilting voice, as though everyone knew that "true love" was a joke, a hoax played on the very young or the very naive.

He frowned. His silence was unnerving, but his nearness was overwhelming as he placed a hand on the table and leaned over her shoulder to peer discriminately at Sir Rodney.

He shook his head. "He's no dragonslayer," he said, using his other hand to spread her pictures out on the table. He leaned over her now, corralling her stampeding emotions between his strong arms. Stray wisps of her fragrant hair caught on the roughness of his beard and his warm breath fluttered other tickling strands at her temples. She was afraid he could hear the quickening of her pulse. "We wouldn't want the beautiful princess at the mercy of the dragon." His voice was a low crooning rumble and titillatingly near. "I have an idea of what Princess Margo is like, and I don't think Sir Rodney is right for her." He turned his face toward her.

His long lashes rose to reveal dark mesmerizing depths, warm, dark pools that beckoned, promising to transport her into a different age and time. They threatened to sweep her into the romantic days of yore, where one longing look was a pledge of love and a promise of ecstasy. She rolled her chair back to break away from the circle of his arms and his spell.

"You haven't seen the knight in action yet," she said, defending Rodney. She pulled out a stack of drawings from a shelf under the table, placed them in a binding frame, and began to flip through the pages. Tony settled around her once more. His nearness was exquisitely disturbing, yet she would have been

59

illogically disappointed if he hadn't surrounded her again. As the pages flipped by, she watched the dark, curling hair form intricate patterns on Tony's muscled forearms and on his long, steady hands that propped him up against the table. She inhaled the spicy scent of the captain's aftershave as Sir Rodney rode into battle on a charging white steed.

Royal blue and scarlet colors fluttered from his helm as the armored rider leaned into the foe, holding his shield and rein in one hand and brandishing a deadly, long-shafted halberd in the other. The flat-topped iron helm protected the knight's head with only an improbably small horizontal rectangle for his view and a chain mail hauberk protecting his arms as he lowered his shining spear into attack position. Charging, the horse moved smoothly under the knight while he lowered the halberd to strike the chest of his opponent.

Details and movements flashed by as Maureen peeked at Tony DiRocco's chiseled profile while he concentrated fully on the action before him. She started her visual journey at the long thick lashes that partially hooded the constantly moving brown eyes, down the plane of his long, straight nose to the determined line of his mouth and his firm, stubborn chin. The woman in her stood intrigued by the angles and planes of his face and the interesting tones and textures of his skin. His high cheeks were smooth, almost tender, but his shadowy, bearded jaw and chin were rough. The artist in her speculated on whether she could capture those qualities in a sketch.

Sir Rodney drew his sword from its leather scabbard and lifted his shield while parrying blows with the gauntlets on his forearms and fending strikes with the ailettes at his shoulders. He slashed justly with his broad sword while his steed pranced at close quarters, head down and nostrils flaring. The rider urged on his mount with his prick spurs, and horse and rider spun in a flurry of offensive lashes. The shield dropped momentarily to bring the wrought metal cuirass protecting the crusader's chest glinting in full dramatic view as another and another mighty blow were struck with the wide sword. Tony DiRocco whistled low when the sketches finally lay motionless.

"That was terrific," he stated irrevocably. "You're very good." He looked at Maureen, amazed. "But I still can't believe that these two are the same person," he said, alternately tapping the lively stack of framed sketches and the drawing of Sir Rodney.

"You think you're capable of sizing up this character that quickly?" she asked with mock offense. She really couldn't consciously defend the pasty knight.

"It's an occupational hazard." He nodded. "I have to know people in my line of work. At times my life depended on it. I've also been able to size you up," he said, allowing his eyes to take in her full length. "I can't believe you're the nonviolent person you claim to be, when you can draw a battle scene like this with so much emotion," he said, arching a dark brow.

"That's preposterous!" She bristled.

"There's too much fire under all that ice," he said. She could feel him watching her. "You're really a closet brawler."

"Only a dumb cop would come up with a ridiculous theory like that," she fussed.

"You may not like violence, but you understand it."

"I do not!" She pushed away from the table, rolling out of his sphere of accusations and magnetic power. "I abhor it." How could such an aggravating man be so appealing? He grabbed the arms of her chair and glided her back to face him.

"What's the matter, don't you like all these psychological theories? Isn't that what the shrinks say about people who make violent movies?"

"This is not a violent movie," she declared with as much moxie as she could muster. "It's for children."

"Not violent? Axes and swords!" he croaked. "Mickey Mouse this is not."

"Guns are obscene, Captain—"

"You have to keep reminding yourself I'm a cop, don't you?" he asked pointedly.

"Frankly, I need no reminders." She lied boldly and loudly.

"I thought you liked these little psychological chats. What's the matter, don't I talk as nice as your good doctor friends?" he needled her. "You'll have to forgive a poor dumb cop who doesn't know how to talk nicely to a lady. Since I usually don't *talk* much with ladies. I much prefer to just . . ."

61

"Yes, I can well imagine," she interrupted him angrily, stopping his colorful comments.

"Oh?" He smirked. "Believe me it would be better than anything you've imagined, Maureen." The use of her first name startled her. "But it's nice to know you've been thinking about me," he teased with an arched brow. He was unbearably close and vitally sexual, and she hated his arrogance.

"I—I—I didn't say that . . . mean that!" she spluttered, and tried to push him away. "I haven't been thinking about you. You're so crude . . . and a cop!"

"What's the matter," he shot back. "Only doctors turn you on?"

Before she knew it, her hand flashed up to smash into his handsome face. He caught her wrist in mid-swing, forcing it back down to the arm of the chair, while trapping her other hand as well.

"Ah, ah, ah. We don't want to get violent here." He soothed her with mock patience. Her wrists were held to the chair by his strong hands and he leaned over her. Putting the weight of his torso on his powerful straight arms, he braced his legs against her legs, protecting himself from an angry female avenger. She stammered a reply, then stopped and stared at him with fire leaping from her eyes as she tried to wriggle free of his grasp. Her high bosom rose and fell with every ragged breath she took, and she tried to shrink back as he leaned closer still. His mouth was only a breath above hers and she couldn't think, all she could do was feel. The blood was rapidly draining from her face. She thought for a moment she would faint if she didn't feel so very much alive in every atom of her body.

"You're the most beautiful cop-hater I've ever seen," he said huskily.

"Let me go!" She hated his self-righteousness, yet all she could imagine were his kisses and embrace. The brown eyes melted her arguments. "Let me go, please," she whispered as she swallowed her protests.

"Why weren't you booked after the riots?" he asked, stunning her again.

"I don't understand. . . ."

"There's no record of your arrest."

"You . . . you . . ."

He released her, stepping back as if he were expecting her to fly away like a freed bird.

"The names Maureen Ryan and Maureen McClure were kicked out of the computer. Along with A K A Mary, Mo, and Molly. That means you have no arrest record."

"How did you . . . ?" She massaged her wrists where he had held her.

"You've been checking up on me!" she accused him, looking at him with indignation. "How dare you?"

"A man in my position has to protect his reputation, lady. I couldn't afford to be sharing a house with a known felon or a fugitive from the FBI, now, could I?" There was an emotion hidden deep in his eyes and almost audible in his voice, but she couldn't read it. He wouldn't let her as he turned away.

"Oh!" she bellowed. "You . . . you . . ."

"Now, we couldn't have a wee lass like yourself taking the heat," he intoned with a brogue as he swung to the attack again. "Could we, now? Some kindly old police captain called your daddy when he recognized your bonnie name, isn't that right?" Maureen twirled out of her chair, escaping his third degree as a flush crept up from beneath her sweater and stung her cheeks.

"That's it!" he concluded from her reaction. "Your old man had some pull, and got you off! But why was a well-respected, well-connected Irishman's daughter shaming her parents by participating in such a spectacle? And what did your husband, Kevin, say when he picked you up from the police station? What would make you do such a thing?"

"Get out of here!" she hissed, crossing her arms over her chest. He couldn't have gotten all that information from a computer. She resented his accuracy and his invasion into her past life. All he had left out was her horrible feeling of isolation, a sense of abandonment that only the rejection of family gave a person.

"Because you're a dreamer. That's what makes you special," he said. "You're also a fighter. Back then you tried to live your dreams and make them come true. Now you just draw them."

"Get out!"

He walked very slowly across the living room, completely unrushed by her fury. He tossed his parting shot over his shoulder. "Your Sir Rodney will never slay that dragon. Never. He won't make it as a knight." He turned to give her one last scathing head-to-toe visual check. "He looks more like an orthodontist." The last word held contempt.

"Out!"

"Here, let me close the doors for you," he said infuriatingly serenely. The doors rolled together. "I know how busy you are," he teased before he pushed the doors together in the middle of the archway with a knock. The doors popped open once more and he watched her intently. "A kind old Irish captain, huh?" he mused. "You're lucky, princess. If I ever found you in my lock-up, I'd never let you go." The doors closed again, breaking the contact between the dark brown eyes and the fire-breathing blue ones as a pelting handful of pens clattered against the door and fell plopping silently onto the living room carpet.

CHAPTER FIVE

Maureen gently laid her pen down on her drawing table even though she had the urge to toss it. She couldn't afford to throw her pens, even under extreme harassment by a flamboyant police captain. She smiled, remembering how her new tenant had aggravated her so. That bout had broken several of her more expensive drawing pens and had disrupted her concentration for the past several days.

Antonio DiRocco's critique of her and her knight flitted through her mind along with his own impressive image. He did have her pegged pretty well; maybe she did take herself too seriously, but maybe it was because all the men she'd known never really did. To her father and brothers she was a pampered little doll. To Kevin she was cute and cuddly and shouldn't worry her little head about anything. Take it easy! The only thing Kevin was intense about was football. Heroes! She studied the sketches of her own elusive knight—part-time gorilla and part-time orthodontist.

Somehow she'd created Sir Rodney as a cross between the Incredible Hulk and a blond Mr. Rogers. She could hardly look at him without laughing. His expression was sincere yet unconvincingly heroic, and his hulking frame skulked and strutted stiffly on the page. Perhaps that was it. Maybe Rodney was too big, too muscle-bound, not quick and agile like a knight, being an expert swordsman and rider, would need to be. She cautiously modified the drawings, trimming brawn and restructuring biceps and shoulders. Yes, Sir Rodney was taking shape now, unlike her nebulous feelings.

She hadn't seen Tony since their fiery parting the day he moved in, yet she was acutely aware of his presence in the house. Inexplicably, she was unconsciously attuned to his schedule, knowing that he worked a lot of overtime. So she knew he took his job very seriously, no matter how cavalier he seemed. She was surprised when he came home early tonight. The lights in his apartment had been on only a short while when Nicki went to visit him, despite her mother's objections.

Maureen continued to contour Sir Rodney, debating, calculating, until Antonio DiRocco and Nicki stalked into the sitting room. When she saw him casually dressed in slacks and a long-sleeved sport shirt, she knew she'd made the right choices on Sir Rodney. The captain moved across the room with supple ranginess. He moved with total confidence and pride, like any knight would—like Sir Rodney should.

"We decided to take you out for Coke and pizza," Nicki declared, preceding Tony like a loyal page. "We've all worked long and hard enough today."

"But I—"

"We insist," Nicki said, getting a nod from Tony.

"But I—" Maureen smoothed her hair back with one hand and trailed the other over her amethyst-colored slacks.

"You look fine. Doesn't she look fine, Tony?" Nicki ventured.

"Very nice," Tony agreed cautiously, but the tilt of his head and the sweep of his eyes over her cream silk blouse up to her full pink lips told more of his appreciation.

"You'll see, Mom, your drawing will go better after you get back," Nicki promised.

Maureen glanced again at Tony, his broad shoulders leaning against the archway, nonchalantly challenging her to take the dare. She pledged she would be lighthearted as she got up from her table. To everyone's surprise—including her own—she smiled and said, "Yes, I think you're right."

Nicki squeaked her excitement and approval. "Wow! That's terrific! I'll be ready in a minute," she said, charging off. Maureen faced the captain alone for a moment.

"One can't work all the time or they'll take themselves too seriously." She shrugged. "I'll get my purse," she said, suddenly feeling wooden.

"Sure." She could feel his eyes on her as she stepped into the entry hall. Maureen got her purse from the halltree, applied a fresh coat of lipstick, and questioned the motives of the woman in the mirror.

"I'm really glad you could go out tonight," Tony called from the sitting room. "I know a great place for pizza. We'll have a good time." He hesitated. "It'll be good for both of us to relax a little bit, you know?"

"Yes. I know." She stepped to the archway to see his torso braced over her sketches on sturdy arms with his fingers spread out on her drawing table. The strangest feeling overcame her, as though she had dreamed of this moment before. He belonged there, looking dark and natural in cinnamon and spice colors. His cuffs were folded up precisely and his rust-colored shirt was tucked neatly into his belted tan slacks. He stood with most of his weight on one leg, and his narrow hips jutted to one side.

"I see you're doing some reconstruction work on Sir Rodney."

"Some," she agreed, studying him. A perfect picture of Sir Rodney's ideal shape sprang into her mind, and she hoped she would be able to remember the image until she had a chance to sketch it.

"Is he going to be a real dragonslayer?"

"Of course."

"I'm sorry about spouting off the other day," he said, meeting her eyes head-on. "I've been told I try too hard to be a policeman twenty-four hours a day."

"Around the clock is too long for any job," she smiled, "even for one you love."

"I hope you and I can have a truce," he said, intentionally leaving his statement open for her positive reply.

"I . . . I . . ."

"You don't want to see this poor little child torn between the two of you, do you?" Nicki asked, vying for sympathy from her mother as she made for the sitting room.

"You're not a child, remember?" Maureen reminded the precocious soul. "I suppose for this poor little waif's sake we could sign a peace treaty. But, please, Captain, don't encourage her, or she'll be camped on your doorstep."

"Mother!"

"She's no bother, really."

"See? I keep telling you, I'm just a warm, wonderful kid."

"Hmmm. You're a con artist."

"Ready?" he asked, leaning casually on the oak archway, enjoying the playful banter between mother and daughter. "I promised Nicki the best pizza in the universe."

"Do you always deliver on all your promises, Captain?" She meant the quip to be smug and sophisticated, but his engulfing gaze took the sting from her words.

"Always," he pledged with only a hint of a smile.

"Wow!" Nicki breathed. "Just like in the movies," she oozed, her wide blue eyes looking from one adult to the other.

"Best in the world," he tempted, arching a dark brow.

"How can you pass that up, Mom?"

How indeed? Maureen swallowed. "I'm ready," she said, cautiously turning to slip on the coat he held for her.

The drive downtown with Tony was an exciting adventure; he knew the city so well and related tales and funny experiences he'd had in different places while on duty. They parked the car near the Water Tower and walked a short distance to the small but crowded pizzeria that had everything from vegetarian, made with whole wheat and tofu, to California-style pizza. They were having a very good time together; they were a harmonious trio, Nicki chatty and earnest, Tony relaxed yet protective, and Maureen playing a casual accompaniment, pretending not to be mesmerized by Tony's tenor-sax voice and dark, shining eyes. Suddenly Nicki left the table in a whirlwind of giggles, pretending to succumb to the lure of the video games.

"I'll be back in time for the pizza," she promised over her shoulder, but she gave them both a wise smile before she left.

"I can't believe it's almost Thanksgiving," Maureen said, attempting to fill the silence looming between them after Nicki's departure. She had the sinking feeling she would be babbling about the weather before the night was over. Tony watched Maureen, who still looked in the direction Nicki had gone, as though she were abandoned. "Time really flies."

"So we must be having fun." He gave her a curious smile when she peered into his face and she couldn't help smiling in return. She felt shy and unprepared somehow to meet the challenge he posed. But his eyes, when she dared look, were sympathetic and kind. Did he really understand her panic? Distractedly she glanced toward the video machines. "Kids today." She shrugged.

"It's not like it used to be," he added.

"Pac-Man and Frogger are like foreign invaders," she agreed, chancing to look into his face to test her theory. She shook her head. "Punk rock, disco dancing, football in the spring . . ." His expression told her she had found a fellow believer with his small shy smile—the one she trusted.

"Do you remember when Christmas season used to begin after Thanksgiving, instead of after Halloween?"

"Yes." She laughed. The ice broke. "The good old days before artificial trees."

"Hmmm." He studied her.

"One thing never changes though—all those gorgeous decorations on the streets and in the store windows downtown. I love that time of year, don't you? My parents used to take all of us kids downtown to see them," she said, not waiting for his reply. "It's a wonderland."

"I remember nights like that. One Christmas when I was about nine Marshall Field's had this fantastic display of electric trains—it seemed like thousands of them—rolling through their own little world in the front windows, over snow-covered hills and towns, through tunnels, over bridges—the works. I stood with my nose pressed to the glass, watching the switches and figure-eights until I needed to be chipped loose from the window."

How long had it been since an attractive man made her laugh? Forever? How long had it been since she had enjoyed a man's company? "You mean you wanted to be a railroader?" she asked, deciding it had been much too long.

"I was a sucker for the steel wheels," he answered, "not to mention being hooked on the striped cap and red bandanna."

"Surely you wanted to be a policeman when you were little?" she teased.

"Actually I was always expected to go into business with my father. Kind of an unspoken pact between him and my mother. I guess I expected that too. But it didn't work out that way." She was listening for the husky catches in his voice, studying its inflections and rhythmic pauses. "So what did little Maureen McClure want to be when she grew up?"

"At nine, I believe I was still searching for that perfect kingdom that had a vacancy for a princess."

"Nothing like starting at the top."

"Sure." She grinned. "But the job of being regal, loving, and wise—"

"And marrying the handsome prince?"

"Something like that," she agreed, melting from his warm gaze and concentrating on her hands for a moment. "You don't find many openings like that."

"That's too bad. You would've been just right for it," he inserted smoothly before the waitress set down the soft drinks and beer on the table and hustled away again. "So what was it like growing up with the most well-known gridiron clan in Chicago? I bet they took care of their little sister?"

"Yes, after they got over their disappointment. I was supposed to be a fullback to even up the sides." She laughed. "But they never let me play, because I was too—"

"Too much like a little doll." His tone smiled but his eyes were serious as she glanced at him before she lowered her eyelids. "I bet those four guys kept a close eye on pretty little Maureen when she got about Nicki's age."

"It wasn't all that necessary. Most boys my age were star-struck by the Notre Dame team and the NFL pros."

"But I can imagine they kept the riffraff away."

"They kept everyone away!" She laughed.

"Didn't you know that's why God invented brothers?" She smiled and agreed, yet at the same time she wondered where Tony had been in those days and conjured how he could have fit into her life so many years ago. "Were you interested in sports?"

"No, not really." He acknowledged her relieved smile. "I just know about a brother's responsibilities. I have a sister that claimed I protected her too much. But I don't think so."

"Hmmm. I see." She pictured him rocky and lean, a tough obstacle to any would-be suitor, yet at the same time was convinced that not even a mountain of big brothers would have deterred Antonio DiRocco. "Brothers!" She chuckled nervously, feeling his radar reading her thoughts. "Most boys were petrified or intimidated by them at the very least."

"All but Kevin Ryan."

"Kevin?" His statement surprised her and she realized for the first time that Derry and Chuck weren't around to protect her when Kevin picked her up and carried her off the day she first met her future husband. "He must have earned their seal of approval?" She wondered if they were around, whether A, B, C, and D would have scared Kevin away too.

"He was like my brothers in a way." She skirted his question. "He was a football hero on the Illinois State campus."

"Naturally, and you were the homecoming queen, right?"

"Hardly. I was into displaying my independence from my parents and the world in general. I was a pseudo-intellectual, majoring in art and fooling with politics."

"And the lovely campus radical met the handsome football star and you fell in love at first sight."

"Something like that."

"And no other men have been in your life since?" He gauged her reaction carefully.

"There've been a few." She looked down to break his intense regard. "But the responsibility of a readymade family isn't appealing to most men."

"And most men won't do when you're interviewing for Prince Charming."

"One prince was enough." She laughed.

"So prince Kevin gave you his fraternity pin and you were campus sweethearts."

"Yes." She smiled, feeling her cheeks warm over how naive and simple she had been. "He reminded me of my brothers . . . he was a gridiron star all right. He lived to play football," she said simply. "He stopped playing forever when he went to Vietnam." She stared down, twisting the gold band on her finger. They seemed to be hovering over unsteady and untested ground,

71

Maureen cautious, but Tony unwilling—or not ready yet—to retreat.

"I was prime material for that war, since I was the right age and already had military training in the police academy. But the draft board evidently decided I could serve better here."

"I'm very glad you weren't sent." She knew her tone was too reflective and sincere, but she couldn't retrieve her words or clearly define the flood of gratitude she felt.

"So your mother and daddy would pack up the whole clan and march you down to see the magic of Christmas a-comin'," he intoned with shades of an Irish brogue entreating her away from her thoughts.

"Ummm-hmmm," she agreed, shaking off the dark mood, thankful for his lightness. "The whole city is like a fairyland at Christmas, twinkling and bright." She was suddenly embarrassed at being caught feeling like a kid. "Nicki and I always go down the evening after Thanksgiving. Tradition, you know," she said apologetically.

"I'd like to see that world with you and Nicki. The holidays have a different slant for cops." He hesitated at the silence. "But I'll probably have to work."

"It's really kind of silly to go anymore," she rationalized, unable to explain her disappointment. "Nicki is nearly all grown up, so I won't have an excuse to go downtown for the holidays. It's really for children, you know."

"For children and dreamers," he agreed quietly.

"Are you a dreamer, Tony?" Her question came out so naturally and fresh, his name rolling freely from her lips, that it turned up his mouth in that devastatingly delicious private smile.

"I used to be," he nodded. His regard renewed a tint of pink in her cheeks, but he voluntarily turned away. "So, do you suppose Nicki's had enough of video games?"

"She never has enough! But I'm sure she'll be designing computers someday soon. She really amazes me!" Maureen said, shaking her head. "I mean she comes off like just an ordinary kid some days, like when you brought her home, but she's really got a head on her shoulders. She's really bright, if I must say so myself. I guess what amazes me is that she's my kid."

72

"She's really special. You've done a great job raising her, especially alone."

"Thank you." She accepted the compliment graciously and the unspoken apology as a token of a permanent peace. "She's a math and science whiz. I've no idea where that came from."

"Ah, but she's got her mother's blue eyes. She'll need several brothers looking after her. But even more important"—he paused—"she's got her mother's imagination. Without it she'd become just another button-pusher." She was mesmerized by his earnestness. His eyes flickered darker, a devouring, shining black, as the intensity of his gaze gently burned away her smile. "I'll go bring the space voyager back to earth. The pizza will be here soon," he said, rising from the table.

"Yes, thank you," she said, recovering.

Nicki's chatter about school, girlfriends, video games, and home computers continued in a steady stream on the way home, even as they pulled into the driveway and got out of the car.

"Tony, can you come in for a minute," Nicki asked when he escorted them to their back door. "Wouldn't that be okay, Mom?"

"Certainly," Maureen agreed as the trio stepped into the welcoming warmth of the kitchen.

"Thank you for taking me along tonight." Nicki giggled. "It was really fun." She beamed at Tony, his pleasure obvious.

"You're welcome. We'll go again sometime. We'll set up a date."

"A date!" Nicki lifted her brows and her voice. "Well, I have a bit more homework to do. Have to keep the grades up, you know." She headed for the door. "But you two can chat awhile longer. Good night."

Maureen and Tony watched the door swing a moment longer before they faced each other again.

"She's a great kid."

"And about as subtle as a Mack truck." Maureen sighed. Tony agreed quietly as he studied her in the silence that followed. They both started to speak at once, then Maureen began again.

"It was a very nice evening. Thank you." He was still watching her carefully. Maureen laughed, rolling her eyes and catching

73

her lower lip between her teeth. "Suddenly I feel like I'm on a date back in high school," she said.

"I know what you mean," Tony chuckled. "I was just trying to decide whether I'd get my face slapped if I were to kiss you good night." His smile faded and he was much too serious as his regard fell on her suddenly dry lips. She didn't quite meet his eyes before turning away nervously, shedding her coat and going to the stove to hook the tea kettle over a finger and take it to the sink to be filled.

"Would you like some coffee?" she said as casually as she could. Her heart was pounding, so she knew she probably spoke too loudly. He stepped behind her.

"Wahl . . . wahl, wahl, listen, ma'am," he drawled in a decent Jimmy Stewart. "No coffee . . . no coffee." He took the kettle from her and set it by the sink. "I—I—I really don't want any, ah, coffee," he said, guiding her from the kitchen into the sitting room all the while bumbling in his impersonation. She was laughing as he sat her down at the table, everything waiting just as she had left it.

"How do you do that? You're really very good, you know." She giggled.

"Aw, shucks, ma'am. You ain't seen nothin' yet." He smiled down at her.

"How do you know all these voices?"

"When I can't sleep I watch a lot of old movies." His smile retreated again. "A lot of old movies. I'll let you get back to work again." He backed away from her with his hands in his coat pockets. "Good night." He turned and walked toward the kitchen.

"Tony?" He stopped and partially faced her as she rose and walked over to him. "You could go through these doors," she said, indicating the large double doors, "so you don't have to go out in the cold again."

"That would be nice." He nodded, but he stood in silence while she unlocked them, his hands still jammed into his pockets. "Good night again." He nodded after Maureen slowly rolled the doors open.

"Tony?" She swallowed.

"Yes?"

"Did you decide against it?"

"Against what?"

"Kissing me good night."

"Believe me, that wasn't my first choice. I'm all the way down to Plan C," he said honestly.

"What was Plan A?" she inquired.

He moved breathtakingly near her. "It goes something like . . ." He started to explain, but he didn't finish as his mouth hovered above hers, her lashes fluttered down, and his lips found her tender mouth. The warm, gentle, unassuming caress of his lips on hers eased them into another world, another time, when kisses were not blatantly stolen and not lightly given on the herb garden path in the shadow of the castle wall. With eyes closed she could breathe in the spicy aroma. When her eyes opened to focus, his black velvet gaze blocked her thoughts and the tiny smile that tugged on the corners of his mouth made her stomach curl in pleasant anticipation.

"Plan A is very nice," she breathed. She meant to sound sophisticated and witty, but her voice quivered nearly as much as her legs. He studied her carefully, as if he weren't listening to what she said, but assessing her with his radar.

His hand smoothed over her cheek to her delicately curved ear and down her creamy throat, until both hands pulled her shoulders closer to him. He tilted his head, questioning her an instant, then gently tasted her lips with a testing kiss as he pulled her commandingly into his arms, enveloping her with powerful bands that kindled her senses and sent her thoughts flying. Who was this bold stranger who dared enter her protected kingdom, to make her laugh, turn her head, take a kiss? He accepted the caress that was all too freely given, as his tongue flicked over her lips, seeking entrance, while his hands glided down her spine. She was flirting with danger as her senses took off in a spiral of sparkling flight in the blackness behind her closed lids. His knowing hands flowed over her back, making her feel desired, the princess, blasting her like a glittering Roman candle through the ages of his kiss.

She was now a captive of her long-imprisoned passions set free by this reckless Romeo who sent waves of vibrations through her. Beware princess! Beware! A warning whined in her ears, distant at first, and then very loud, and she wrenched herself away from him.

"It's okay. It's just my pager," he assured her huskily, looking down into her wide blue eyes. "I have to make a call," he said, turning off the electronic pager hooked onto his belt. "You're saved by the bell."

"Me, saved?" she said, trying to recover from the quivering-to-the-toes kiss. "You were the one on the ropes, Captain."

"Maybe you're right." His smile along with his sweeping regard were too personal, and she could feel heat rising up from her throat. His handsome features and dark eyes were convicting her of being a silly dreamer and of being naively susceptible to his charms. "I really have to say good night now. Usually a call this time of night means more work. But I'd like to go out with you again, Maureen, if . . ."

"If it works out." She nodded.

"Fair enough."

"Good night."

"Yes, Maureen," he answered to some unspoken question. "Good night."

It was only a few minutes later, while she sat at her drawing table, that she heard him leave the house, charging into the darkness. But she was amazed at how much smoother her drawings went and how many she got done.

It never ceased to amaze Maureen how accurate her hindsight was—always 20/20. She should have known better than to go out to eat with him, to talk with him, to laugh at his jokes and share memories, to allow his mellow voice to haunt her thoughts, and to permit his kiss to burn through her. When would she ever learn? When would she see these things coming before they reached up and slapped her in the face, waking her rudely from her dreams.

It had been several days since she saw him, including hours of thinking and trying to forget, so she had plenty of time for her vision to clear again. Nicki relayed to Maureen that Tony was very busy on the weekend, something about the full moon. Maybe Maureen could blame her romantic notions on the golden Illinois harvest moon also. But at least not seeing Tony gave her time to reorganize her shattered defenses.

She continued to remind herself how her romantic fantasies caused her trouble before. Her love for Kevin Ryan had blinded her to the fact that she and Kevin were so different from each other. She and Tony were already starting out at opposite ends of the spectrum. Yet her thoughts would stray as she drew at her table; her eyes would sneak away from her work and check the time, the window, the double oak doors. He was working late again, she knew by her own instinctive sensing device. He left for dinner hours ago and hadn't returned, but he would return soon. He could even be holding her in his arms again soon, kissing her. . . . She was startled back to her sketches by the sound of his car pulling into the driveway. She concentrated very hard on her work, punishingly so, to chase away all the sensual thoughts, until she heard a knock on the door.

Antonio DiRocco stood at her back door dressed for work— neat, handsomely attired. She suspected that he was one of those men who always looked exceptional in a business suit—sexy, in control, wise. Along with the cool November air, she could feel Tony's magnetism coming up on her emotional blind side as he stepped into the kitchen.

"Thanks for letting me in. I saw your light in the window." He spoke almost apologetically, then he smiled. "It's nice seeing you."

"You must have been called out again."

"Yes, nothing serious though," he said, gliding past her to lean against the kitchen counter. "No real harm done. The officers at the scene thought it might turn into a media thing, and they were right." He smiled, rubbing his jaw. "Two plucky eighty-three-year-old gents decided to have a duel. Fortunately neither of them could see well enough or were strong enough to really aim the guns." He gave her a wry grin. "They may be asked to leave their apartment though." He was looking too confident, too magnetic. His voice sounded too mellow as he braced himself against the counter with his hands in his coat pockets.

"See how dangerous guns can be? What happened?"

"It seems it was a crime of passion, of course. Both roommates were dating the same charming younger woman. She's seventy-nine."

"You're never too old, I guess." Maureen chuckled.

"Never." His gaze lingered on her cheeks and lips for a moment, and his smile creased his cheeks. "Are you still drawing?" He slipped his watch from his pocket and checked the time as she enjoyed the sounds of his rustling coat and the tinkling chain of his watch. Her eyes were drawn from his movements to meet his devouring gaze. "It's late."

"I'm afraid I work police-captain hours." She shrugged gracefully and tried to smile.

"Are you going to be working awhile longer?"

"I think so," she said. "Are you going to watch a movie?"

"I'd rather watch you draw."

"I really don't think . . . I mean, it's not nearly as exciting as a movie."

"Oh," he conceded, "in that case, you can watch me draw," he said, grasping her hand and leading her into the sitting room. "That's real entertainment."

"You draw?" Maureen laughed.

"Yes, of course. Don't laugh!" he said earnestly, shedding his coat and flipping it over the back of a chair as he marched her through the dining room. "Besides, you haven't seen my work yet," he said indignantly, taking her by the shoulders and setting her down at the drafting table. He eased onto the stool beside her as Maureen moved her sketches aside and Tony picked up a pad, waving both arms artistically over the empty page.

"Okay, little lady! What will it be? Mystery, western, spy thriller?"

"Western," she decided, ready for the new adventure.

"Ah, a soft spot for the ol' horse operas. That's good."

"Just call me a hopeless romantic," she said. "I like it when the good guys win and all that."

"I see."

"Who do you want? I can draw them all. The Duke? Gary Cooper? Hank Fonda?"

"Ummm. How about John Garfield?"

"Garfield? Very good!" he said, obviously impressed. "So you watch old movies too?"

"Umm-hmm, sometimes."

"I don't remember Garfield playing too many cowboys, but . . ."

78

"Maybe he should have," she teased, but his sparkling eyes met hers and she looked back at his hands. "Besides, a man of your talents should enjoy the challenge."

"Of course," he said, waving his arms as a prelude to the grand artistic event. Then he settled his hand and the tip of the pen onto the page. "He'll be the good guy—the sheriff."

"Naturally," she agreed, "a man standing alone against the odds, fighting for truth and justice."

"Right." He paused, watching her, and started a circle near the center of the page, then a long single line for the body branching diagonally, forming legs. Maureen pressed her fingers to her mouth, stifling her laughter until her body was shaking. "Don't laugh! I'm not done yet." With flair he shaped cowboy boots with asterisks as spurs that nearly met each other, and added a large star on the chest of his stick figure. A horizontal line served as arms, and another, with a horseshoe on top, formed a ten-gallon hat held up by sugar-bowl-handle ears on the round head. She couldn't contain her laughter any longer.

"I'm sorry. I don't want to break your concentration." She giggled her apology as Tony put in the round eyes, banana nose, and short, straight line for the mouth.

"Are you laughing at my masterpiece?" he asked, playing tough and turning toward her. "Hey, are you laughing?" he teased, chuckling. His free hand brushed by her braid and gently massaged her nape. His contented look encompassed her like sunshine on a rainy day, and she leaned toward him, soaking in his energy. "I like to hear you laugh, you know that? It sounds good."

"It feels good." She sighed, leaning her head on his shoulder as his arm automatically came around her and his hand glided down her arm.

"I agree."

"I like your sheriff's eyes," she said, settling down to an occasional titter.

"But it's all in the hat and spurs," he said, welcoming her body next to his. Maureen relaxed against him, succumbing to his warmth and energy until she suddenly realized how good it felt to bask next to his sensual body, cradled by his strong arm, and she self-consciously sat up, embarrassed.

"Meanwhile, back at the ranch," Tony intoned, covering her shyness. "This sheriff has run a tight ship for years, right?"

"Right."

"No one messes around with him or his town. Everybody knows they have to toe the line, or else the sheriff will have to set them straight. Until one day—"

"Until the James gang rides into town to rob the—"

"No, no, no."

"The Daltons?"

"No . . ." Tony started another circle lower and smaller than the first, but instead of a straight line for a body he drew a small inverted triangle, whose point met with the tip of a taller upright triangle with high-heeled shoes beneath. "Until . . . the new schoolmarm comes to town."

"With an hour-glass shape, I see."

"A very nice little shape," he agreed, giving her an appraising, rakish grin. "But, of course, she's more than just a pretty package; she has grit. She's mini but mighty and takes a hard line on what she believes is good for the schoolchildren. Yet she's as lovely and delicate as a China doll . . . a beautiful smile." He drew a single curved line. "Gorgeous lake-blue eyes." He penned in the circles and long dark lashes.

"It sounds like the sheriff could be in for trouble."

"Deep trouble," he agreed without looking at her as he continued with details on the spunky schoolmarm. "Altogether, she's more of a burr under his saddle than all the roughest, toughest hombres north or south of the Pecos. He can handle shooters and rustlers. But the schoolmarm's something else—a real Grace Kelly type."

"I don't think Garfield and Kelly ever made a movie together."

"Maybe they should have," he said gravely, sweeping her with a dark velvet regard.

"But they didn't," she insisted, feeling heat coming to her cheeks and panic rising in her throat, fathoming that the sheriff was not the only one in deep trouble.

"Do you know how you knew that?" he pressed confidently. "Because a film with those two would've been unforgettable. A

80

classic." His tone mellowed into a warm rhythm and blues melody that floated to her.

"So what happened to the sheriff then?" she asked, breaking the trance of his Pied Piper voice.

"So, late one night after making his rounds and securing the town, he sees a light in her window. . . ."

"Late one night?" Her wide blue eyes met his inviting dark depths.

"Yeah, like tonight," he answered distractedly. "So the sheriff gets to thinking that standing up for truth and justice isn't so bad, but standing alone is not so good."

"Enter Grace Kelly, I mean the schoolmarm?" She followed his storyline.

"Yeah, he sees the light in her window and he gets to thinking that it would be nice to come home and find—"

"A light?" She slipped out of her chair and moved away from the table.

"Just a light is not quite all he had in mind," he crooned. She could hear the invitation in his voice as he came up behind her. She sensed his warmth when he was close behind her, and his hands rose to gently knead her shoulders. She was willing her body not to respond, but she knew her clear vision would return only in the morning. He bent his head, placing tender, silent kisses on her temples and ears, nipping the lobes with his teeth so lightly that she arched her creamy white neck, inviting another taste. His caresses trailed down her soft velvety skin to the sensitive hollow below her ear. Responding, she pressed gently back into her leather-tough sheriff. She was losing her sight completely as her head eased back against his shoulder and her lids fluttered down. Cautious thoughts abandoned, she could only wonder whether he saw her light, and if he would pull her into his arms. But she couldn't surrender to the fantasy, because that was all it was—a flight of fancy, a seductive illusion . . . But whose?

"The sheriff would be much wiser if he wouldn't . . ." she trailed off. "He's starting something that can't be finished."

"Why not?"

She turned to face him, puzzled that he couldn't see the terrible mistake they would make. "He's the tough guy and she's—"

"She's very soft," he whispered, his lips hovering above hers before his mouth came down on hers, testing, reviving. Did he have any idea what he was doing to her? What chaos he was causing her? One arm cradled her as the other hand started at her rounded hip and drifted up over her ribs to rest near the curve of her breast. Her last coherent thought was that he knew exactly what he was doing. His caress became exquisitely tender, while his tongue flirted past her lips to the honeyed moistness within, completely destroying all her defenses.

Her body melted into his, fitting the soft curves of her breasts against the hard planes of his chest. Her hands ventured haltingly to his shoulders and finally found each other at the nape of his neck, where curious fingers discovered a tangle of soft, curling hair above his crisp collar. Her fingers lingered there, playing in the thick hair, stroking his heated kiss that became more explorative and deep. He lifted his head and she could feel his warm, erratic breath on her temple. She knew she should pull away from his arms, but she leaned against him, not trusting her legs to support her weight as she continued to watch the rockets exploding behind her closed lids.

"See? An unforgettable team," he murmured.

"They're from two different worlds. What could they possibly give each other?"

"Give? You mean besides companionship, trust, and unlimited pleasure?" he asked, surprised. "Well," he drawled, "he could fix all her parking tickets. And she could give him . . . art lessons."

"Art lessons?" she said in a small voice.

"Whadayasay, schoolmarm, ma'am?"

It started slowly at first, but then her laughter rose up. He drew her closer and tenderly rocked her. She laughed with her cheek pressed into his shoulder and returned his hug.

"You're really something else, you know that?" she whispered.

"That's my line," he laughed, giving her an extra squeeze. She relaxed against him, responding to his soft voice and the powerful arms that held her. The firmly muscled body that fit her shape so neatly was the western sheriff, an attractive man, deliciously appealing, yet so different, opposite to her. It was a paradox she wasn't prepared to face, any more than she could unravel the enigma of Antonio DiRocco, tough yet tender.

"But I think we'd better say good night."

"I could just hang around here until we could say good morning."

"I don't think so," she said, slipping from his arms. "It's not a good idea."

"No, it's not a good idea. It's fantastic," he said, lifting her chin with his fingers, but not really making any demands. "We make a good team. Classic." His voice was rough and low, matching the tiny private smile turning his lips.

"Good night, Tony."

"Good night, princess."

CHAPTER SIX

Dreaming and chilled, he stalked through the cool, damp passageway dimly lit with torches. Sensing danger and feeling constraint around his chest, he guessed he wore a bulletproof vest, but he couldn't imagine why he carried his badge in his hand. Inherently he knew he was looking for Maureen Ryan. The place was dank and mystifying, but he was sure he would find her here and be able to wring truthful answers from her.

Since he had first laid eyes on the high-spirited beauty, she had fought him, lying to him on every turn. Yet she made Tony feel totally alive and filled his senses with her wide, innocent eyes as deep and astonishingly blue as Lake Michigan and with her smooth, perfect, floral-scented skin that made him ache to caress her. She filled his thoughts. He couldn't forget her sweet, undisguised surrender in his embrace or how much her sensual pink lips begged for his lovemaking. He would find her in this strange place and talk with her—make love with her. She confused and intrigued him. She was part angel, aloof and innocent, part temptress, all warm and sensuous, pressed against his body, and part child, who drew images of dreams. His usual level-headed attitude and the tough objectivity that he had cultivated all his years on the force melted when he was near her. He thought about her all the time, but now she invaded his subconscious while he slept. Torches lit his way. He would find her.

Although she stubbornly refused to admit her attraction to a policeman, in this fantasy he would find her and make her confess. He would possess her. Love her. In this world of shadows he wasn't afraid of the word. He would love her, like he had loved no other woman—forever.

"Antonio, are you all right?" It was a woman's voice, but it wasn't Maureen's. He was panicked that he couldn't keep hold of her. He had vowed he would love her forever and she was snatched away from him. He loved someone and she was taken away. Didn't he always know that would happen? "Antonio, I didn't mean to startle you," Linda said. "You must have been dreaming." He looked at his sister standing at the foot of his bed and tried to orient himself in this room. He was lost again, but things were rapidly clearing. He knew he was awake now and recognized his small bedroom just below the bedroom of Maureen Ryan. The dream had been so real that he wanted to rush up the oak stair to see if Maureen was there and safe. But how could he explain that he had been dreaming of a horrible castle that held his beautiful princess captive?

"Tony? I just wanted to remind you that we're celebrating Thanksgiving tonight instead of tomorrow because Gerald is leaving for Egypt on Thanksgiving Day. Remember?" She looked at her brother, concerned. "Are you having nightmares about Cluny again? Or Mother?

"No!" He rubbed his face. "The dream was just very real, that's all. What are you doing here?" He was still confused about his sister's presence.

"I didn't mean to startle you. I brought some things that I thought you would need for your new kitchen."

"What?" Tony blinked, rubbing his eyes. He was certain he was awake, yet this conversation smacked of déjà-vu, as though he had dreamed it before. "You came all the way across town from the 'Gold Coast' this early in the morning to bring me, what, a few kitchen things? Linda!"

"I wanted to ask you to dinner in person, without the interruptions of your office, so you would find fewer excuses not to come to visit." She looked at him severely, yet with indominable compassion. "Will you come?"

"You know me pretty well, don't you?"

"I love you, Antonio. You're my brother, my only family. I've two little children who worship and adore you," Linda said enthusiastically. Tony couldn't look at his sister. "You can do everything but walk on water for those little ones. If you don't come for dinner, they'll be extremely disappointed." She wound down, so Tony chanced a glance at her, remembering all the excuses he'd given in the past, flimsy ones at best. Always work. Sometimes he'd even volunteer to work for the other married officers on holidays. It was safer than fortifying ties with his lovely sister, pretending indifference to confuse the fates, for fear she would be taken from him too.

"I have to rush off to work now," Linda said. "You're okay, aren't you? You're not having trouble sleeping again?"

"I'm fine." He looked at his sister and felt bad about frightening her. "But do you mind stepping out of the room. I need to get ready for work too," he said, threatening to throw back the covers twisted around his hips.

"Oh," she said, embarrassed. "I'll start some coffee, okay? I'll leave the key on the kitchen table, and then I have to run. Tonight, okay? Dinner?" Her expression was so hopeful and pleased as she whirled from the room.

"Right." He slipped his naked body from the bed and walked into the bathroom. He stared thoughtfully at the man in the mirror before he stepped into the shower. It was the same stubbly face and hard, truth-seeking eyes he'd faced every morning, but he surmised things were changing inside. He suspected that one loveable teenager and one gorgeous blond dreamer had a lot to do with it.

How real was his dream? Was he really falling in love with Maureen Ryan? All he knew for sure, as the warm water streamed over his body, was that he wanted to make love to her. He wanted to hold and caress her and whisper to her of love in the quiet night. He knew they would be fantastic together. He would love her no matter how many dragons he must slay. He stepped from the shower, scanning his image in the mirror. Definitely knight material, he mused, appraising his sturdy form. *One last crusade and Maureen will be mine.* He dried himself briskly, wrapping his narrow hips with a towel that he twisted into a knot over one hip to secure it before lathering his face to shave.

"Antonio, this is a very nice apartment," Linda called through the bathroom door, breaking his line of thought as he lathered his face. "By the way, who is the princess?"

"What?" he asked, surprised, looking into the mirror over the sink. He questioned the man with the white-foamed face before he put the razor to his cheek again. *She is the woman you love, if you're willing to take the chance,* came the answer.

"Whoever she is, she must be special. You called her name in your sleep," Linda said, abandoning the door to answer the whistle of the tea kettle in the kitchen. He was agreeing with the man in the mirror when a knock came on the large double oak doors.

"I'll get it," he said, wiping the foam hurriedly from his face and heading for the door, flipping the hand towel over his head to hang over his neck. He would open the only barrier that separated him from Maureen Ryan, and he would slay all the dragons.

Maureen was prepared. She had rehearsed the invitation many times in her mind. Nicki had begged, playing on her mother's bleeding heart to invite Tony DiRocco to Thanksgiving dinner tomorrow because the poor man would be all alone. In a weak moment Maureen promised she would ask him, so she planned the no-nonsense, no-frills speech to the finest detail. There were no innuendos and absolutely no doubt that he would be Nicki's guest. She had it down cold as she smoothed the collar of her light-aqua blouse over the delicate neckline of her sweater and slid nervous hands down her darker turquoise slacks. She owed her tenant at least a dinner, Maureen reasoned, and much more. His dinner invitation and late-night visits came as pleasant diversions from sketching. She relaxed, laughed, enjoyed his company. It amazed Maureen how much smoother her sketches progressed after their time together, how much better everything went. But certainly Sir Rodney was coming to life, nearly breathing on his own now. Yes, she owed Antonio DiRocco Thanksgiving dinner at least. He gave her happy moments, warm memories, and at times she wondered if perhaps it was real, not just a fantasy. Could they be that unforgettable classic couple Tony said they were? But she knew she couldn't take the chance of finding out.

She knocked on the high door that separated their living quarters and waited, poised and prepared. She was randomly thinking about things she needed to pick up from the grocery store. Myron always gave her the day before Thanksgiving off so he could come and enjoy her cooking on the holiday. She was prepared, on top of everything, until Tony DiRocco in all his natural splendor opened the door and she was back to dumb-founded babbling.

"Oh!" she uttered, but she couldn't look away. Her eyes were drawn like a magnet to his nearly nude, toned, athletic body. Her brazen gaze swept over him from head to toe, from the dark covering of hair on his broad chest as it thickened down the decline from his ribs to the flat plateau of his abdomen. Gratefully a fluffy brown towel that clung snugly to his narrow hips cut her view as her eyes strayed lower to the strong angular muscles of his thighs and calves.

"May I help you?" he asked, obviously confident that she liked what she saw.

"Yes—no!" Modesty escaped her; she couldn't turn away. A small beige handtowel was folded around the back of his neck, and a long gold chain hung down between his flat brown nipples. An intricately engraved Latin cross dangled from it, playing a glittering game of hide-and-seek in the tangle of dark hair. It was a suitable charm for a golden-skinned knight who fought many battles. He was well-protected, but not unscathed. She noted irregular scars on his arms and one long vertical welt that started above his ribs and went down out of sight.

"The guided tour is more fun," he said with a patient, lazy grin.

"What?" she breathed. "I was going to ask you something, but it can wait until after work." She looked again at the long scar that formed a white track through the tangle of dark hair that didn't quite cover it. "I should be going," she said, turning away.

"No. Don't go again, please!" There was a tone of urgency in his voice as he grasped her arm and pulled her dangerously close.

She disciplined herself to look away from his body. His dark hair was finger-combed and glistening wet from the shower and he smelled clean and absolutely delicious. A breath caught in her throat. There was a small, distracting patch of shaving cream on his high cheekbone, evidently left over from his interrupted shaving.

"You missed a spot," she explained as she reached a timid hand up to scoop the small triangle of foam from his warm face. She abruptly withdrew her fingers, surprised by the roughness of his whiskered skin, a totally unnecessary reminder of his manhood, since his manly attributes were already short-circuiting her senses and her resolve. Instinctively he leaned toward her, consuming her with a dark-eyed gleam that drew her like a magnet. She could feel herself float into his power, where he was the only energy source. She listed toward his vitality, her lips parted, and her skin flushed. She didn't know what she would do if he kissed her. His intensity frightened her and her response to him speeding through her body in a chain reaction was even more petrifying. She retreated slightly, expelling a shaky breath and willing her racing heart to slow its pace as she cautiously pulled one end of the handtowel from his neck until it draped over one shoulder and over one very well-defined pectoral and brushed the shaving cream from her tapered index finger onto the absorbent terry cloth. He watched her every move with deep, nearly black, eyes while a muscle flexed along his jaw. From his tenseness she gathered she must have made him angry, so she flinched when his hand suddenly captured hers.

"Don't let the rough exterior scare you," he said in a sultry tone, gently bringing the back of her graceful hand to his cheek. Responding to his tenderness, she unwisely allowed her hand and fingers to languidly trail over the smoothness to his chin. His eyes mellowed and threatened to swallow her, and she realized that she wanted to kiss his smooth face and his mouth, and longed to press herself against his chest. She started to speak.

"Hmmm." She was alarmed by the clarity and escalating passion of her fantasy. "I really have to get going."

"You wanted to ask me something?" he reminded her, slowing her escape.

"How did you get that scar?" The question popped out before

it even registered in her brain. She was mortified that she was so tactless, but hadn't the conversation between her and the captain always been much too personal? She looked down at the long incision and then up at his chest, then away. He was making her nervous, or was it only her thoughts?

"I got it as a souvenir from a real cop-hater, not a beautiful faker like you," he teased.

"But it's a surgical scar," she said, recognizing the difference between the touch of a surgeon and a violent irregular tear like those on his arms.

"A doctor patched me up."

"What happened?"

"Not much really," he said, hopefully dismissing the question.

"What's not much?" she pressed on, finding a topic Tony actually shied away from. She didn't know how she knew, but she knew. By sound, perhaps, she could recount his pain and visualize the unseen and untold hurt as the laid-back blues song in his voice stiffened into a military cadence. She didn't allow the subject to drop. "Tell me," she urged quietly.

"When I was a rookie on the beat I misjudged what some punks told me. I miscalculated the situation. They got the jump on me and nearly beat me to death." He looked away from her for a moment when he saw fear etched in her features. "But a doctor was able to sew me back together again before I bled to death. That's all." He shrugged. When he finished, an emotion flicked across the bottomless brown eyes, but he didn't give her time to translate it.

"You were very angry," she stated, wondering where the words came from. And then she remembered how furious she had been after recovering from the violation and shock of being pounded with a billy club and thrown into a paddy wagon with other bloodied kids during the riot. Tony surveyed her with undisguised amazement, his body tense.

"Blind outrage comes closer to the right description," he said with just the beginning of a humorless, sarcastic laugh. "Fortunately I had a long time to get myself back together, recuperating." The vertical furrows between his brows deepened and the line of his mouth matched the turned-down corners of his eyes. He readjusted the towel around his neck, keeping hold of both ends, bunching the biceps of his arms as though the isometric pressure against his neck would eliminate the memories. His movement brought a new wave of desire as Maureen continued to survey his body. The predominant veins in his sturdy arms and the developed muscles of his chest and shoulders caused instant fantasies about being held by those arms.

"That's not what you wanted to ask," he crooned, leading her, his dark mood passing nearly as quickly as it came.

"Antonio . . . Antonio?" A woman's voice was calling from the back of the apartment. Maureen questioned Tony's forgetful expression and then stared past his shoulder into the dusk of the hallway. Her legs turned to rubber when a gorgeous dark-eyed woman burst into the morning room. "Antonio, the coffee's ready. I—I didn't know you had company," she said, mildly shocked. She pursed her full, generous mouth, eyeing Maureen's motionless figure. Maureen swallowed a painful lump of disappointment and bitter anger. He had the gall to stand talking to her, making love to her with his eyes, as if he had forgotten there was another woman in his bedroom.

"Linda, this is Maureen Ryan." Tony spoke with infuriating calm, as though he were used to having two lovers in the same room. He probably was! She wondered if a jealous husband or a misguided woman hadn't added to his collection of scars over the years. "Maureen and her daughter, Nicki, are my new landladies."

"Hello." Her voice was black sable.

"Hello." Maureen couldn't think of anything else to say. She could hardly say Nice seeing you here. She wanted a trapdoor to open under her feet so she could disappear from the room, but the floor remained grievously solid.

"I didn't realize you . . ." Maureen directed her words to Tony, who was studying her carefully.

"I understand now why Antonio has been staying so close to home lately." She smiled, giving Maureen an appraising look. Maureen felt her cheeks flush. Linda was dressed impeccably in a toast-brown suit with suede heels to match, her silk blouse and gold jewelry all accentuating the rich tones of her skin and dark eyes. She was stunning. Maureen coveted the woman's sophistication and her man. She was much more cosmopolitan about the whole situation than Maureen would have been. Much more! She didn't know who she was more angry with—Antonio DiRocco or herself. And what made it worse, as she degraded herself for being a first-class jerk, he seemed to be enjoying this whole scenario.

"Antonio, don't forget dinner tonight," Linda said, bussing his cheek. "You missed a spot," she said to him, pointing to the rough patch on his cheek.

"Yes, I've been told." Tony smiled at Maureen.

"It was very nice meeting you, Miss Ryan," Linda said, glancing over her shoulder. Maureen was boiling into a silent rage.

"Yes, likewise," she choked out, her cheeks staining red more deeply.

"I must run," Linda said, scanning the tense young woman and Tony again. "Good-bye, Antonio," she said in a lightly teasing tone. "Good-bye, princess," she tossed to Maureen, and took brisk steps through the hallway and out of the apartment with the couple staring after her.

"That was Linda," he said finally, sizing up her hostility.

"Umm-huh," Maureen grunted, not trusting her voice and pushing back questions that were none of her business, although it didn't take a genius to know what a fantastic-looking woman was doing in the Mediterranean Wizard's apartment. He's no choirboy, despite his long-suffering eyes and playful smile, she concluded.

"Hey!" he laughed, "it's not what you think."

"Strictly business I suppose?"

"Not exactly, but not that personal either."

"Not personal!" she screeched. "You spend the night with a woman and you don't call that personal."

"Believe me, when I make love with a woman, it's very personal. You can count on that," he promised, catching her arm. "But I—"

"Don't touch me," she said, jerking her arm from his grasp.

"Why are you so angry?"

"I'm not angry," she shouted.

"I never said I—"

"I know you aren't a choirboy, Captain DiRocco, but I—"

"But you don't want me to see any women besides you. Right?" He spoke casually.

"Right. No, I didn't say that." Damn his egotistical, pompous, know-it-all attitude. He gave her a smile that put butterflies in her stomach and almost made her forget her anger. "That's not what I meant at all," she lied, and then started with truth. "I resent you bringing your ladyfriends into my house. What if Nicki would see them? She's only a child!"

"Nicki's sensibilities aren't what's eating you, lady," he said, fire kindling in his eyes. "Why don't you just admit it?"

"Contrary to popular belief, you are not irresistible, Captain DiRocco."

"Yeah. Especially since I'm a cop, right?" He nearly shouted at her, gesturing with both hands to emphasize each word. His anger was instant and frightening.

"That's right," she charged. She whirled away from him, running from the room, crossing the seemingly endless pale-green dining room.

"Maureen, wait. Maureen!"

She hesitated only long enough to jerk her coat and scarf from the halltree and to take a last look at the incredible man who could hurt and aggravate her with the greatest of ease. It was grossly unfair that he should look so attractive, and it was cruel and unusual punishment that he should belong to another woman.

"I'm sorry I interrupted your morning, Captain," she said deceptively calmly as she thrust a fist into the sleeve of her coat, clambered into it, and threw her scarf on, flipping each end of it cavalierly back over her shoulders. "I won't do that again," she added, opening the front door and stepping out. She gave the door a mighty slam and took several steps before she was jerked back by her knitted pink scarf caught in the door. She stomped her feet and pounded her fists on her thighs. God, couldn't she even make an angry getaway right? She turned and opened the door again, burst into the entry, grabbed her purse, and glanced at the smiling Antonio DiRocco propped rakishly against the archway. His arms were folded across his broad chest and a knee was bent, a bare foot against the doorframe, showing a disturbing length of golden thigh. She growled her frustration through tightly clamped teeth and tore out of the door again, this time making good her escape.

The biting chill of the November wind was a good excuse for her eyes to water as she hurried along the sidewalk. She was angry with Tony for being so confidently irresistible and outraged with herself for wanting him, like dozens of other women. Like Linda. Just the thought of the beauty made her feel more cold and miserable. There was no way for Maureen to have him. He was taken. But it was better that way, wasn't it? She didn't want him, right? She had made love with a boy once, and so miserably failed to please him, how could she even pretend to keep the attention of a man like Tony, especially since he had so many ardent admirers. Maureen was so drawn to his tightly wrapped body and magnetism; she was positively scared. And he knew it. Damn his radar! She would stay far away from him.

She didn't need those kinds of problems again with a husband who felt ensnared and slighted. She may have attracted her first husband's eye, but in the final analysis her parents had arranged the marriage with the parents of Kevin Ryan. She had snagged the boyish rogue because she just happened to be pregnant with his child, a point which he argued even up until he left for Vietnam.

Their wedding was very proper, private, and quickly arranged, because she was already in her sixth month. She had vehemently refused to say who the father was for months, because she never wanted to see Kevin Ryan again. She abhorred the idea of marrying him, because he wouldn't accept responsibility for their baby. But her parents were nearly sick with worry about the father being a drug-crazed hippie or revolutionary. Her soft heart melted and she told them who the father was. She cringed when her parents were so pleased that the father was such an upright young man, and a football player besides. He could be understood, painfully so. He was very transparent, she had to agree; nothing at all deep or complex had passed between herself and Kevin Ryan.

He had been a fun-loving all-American boy, wild and free. He could have been a model for a surfboard company, and he loved to have a good time, until he felt captured by a wide-eyed woman he had never really taken time to know, already swollen with his

94

baby. Kevin had been too beautiful and young to die. If their marriage hadn't taken place, he would still be alive and she wouldn't be a scared rabbit that felt the snare. She was crippled, but at least she had survived. Kevin had been strongly attracted to her at first also, how well she remembered. But they were opposites in every way, finally trapped in a partnership never destined to work. And now she could see that she was setting herself up for a repeat performance with the dark, irresistible police captain. A performance destined to the same disappointing, painful ending.

She turned the corner to walk past the shops of Austin that faced Bonner Street. She would put her knight in shining armor on a pedestal. He would be charming and say wonderful, witty, warm things until the words became so loving she believed it had all come true. Then the dream would fade one day when her brave knight would say something very stupid like "It's really been great, Mo, but I think we're getting too serious. Lighten up. Have some laughs." "Oh, Lord!" Her small voice was lost in the frigid air. It was better for the bubble to break now, to get Tony DiRocco out of her mind before she lost her heart. But it was already too late.

He was too intense, too violent, too quick-tempered, too . . . How could she allow herself to fall in love with a man like Antonio DiRocco? With all her fighting she still fell for the handsome police captain. She admitted it at last, if only to herself, but she could never admit it to him. He would think it was too funny. A cynical policeman and a bleeding heart. A Lothario and a silly schoolgirl. She wouldn't allow either of them to fall into a tender trap where they would be killing each other with warm words of love turned bitter and cold. She would never abuse herself again that way.

Maureen was still stewing but the tears had stopped when she reached the small grocery store. She nodded at Mrs. O'Neal as she entered the store and picked up a shopping basket, trying to hide her red eyes. She walked to the produce area, where she tried to remember the items she needed for dinner tomorrow. She would explain to Nicki why Tony couldn't come to dinner. Maureen stood staring at the shelves vacantly. She didn't need Tony DiRocco. She didn't want any man complicating her life.

She had healed her wounds, lived her life, and cared for her daughter for fourteen years without anyone's help. So what if she loved him. What was love anyway but a fairy tale for fools?

She didn't need anyone else; she had managed to survive before and she'd do it again. She slammed a couple of yams into the shopping basket. Then why did she feel so miserable and disappointed to know that he belonged to someone else? She felt as smart and tough as the leathery potatoes as she gathered more, carefully placing them into her basket.

He's a cop! A cop of all things. How could she possibly fall for a cop? For an instant she remembered the long scar on his body. He had lived with danger. He was a survivor too.

Hovering over the lettuce bin, Maureen heard a startled Mrs. O'Neal greet someone at the register and saw an intensely professional Tony DiRocco wearing a tan suit, a tie, and his trench coat. He nodded and gave the woman a succinct greeting, and then marched toward the produce section and Maureen. His jaw set and his dark eyes trained on her, he walked toward her with determined strides. She broke the gaze between them and busily concentrated on the Idaho potatoes now, intently ignoring him.

"I need to talk to you, Maureen." His words were sharp and crisp, but his voice still had its sultry sound. All his energy seemed focused on her, and she staggered under its fire until she found her voice at last.

"I don't want to talk to you. I don't want you living in my house. . . ." She lowered her voice as she noticed Mrs. O'Neal's curiosity. "How did you find me?"

"You forget I spent six years as a first-class detective." His gaze was unwavering. "And, besides, in your rush to leave, you dropped your grocery list." He smiled, handing the small paper to her.

"Thank you." She snatched the paper from him. They didn't speak for a moment. She couldn't look at him because his eyes penetrated her, so she kept her head down, her long braid tumbling over one shoulder as she reached for more potatoes.

"Why are you so upset?"

"I'm not upset!" she insisted.

"Then why are you filling your basket with potatoes?" he asked calmly. She looked befuddled at the dozens of spuds heaped into the basket. He took the canvas tote from her numb hands and took out some potatoes.

"I want to know why seeing another woman in my apartment made you so angry?" He put the question flat out. "And I want the truth," he qualified.

"I have a very impressionable daughter, as you may recall," she explained tightly. "What if she saw your girlfriends going in and out of the house? What would she think about her hero then?" She threw the words at him.

"She would think I had a healthy appetite," he said, tilting his head to see her eyes, testing his metaphor.

"And you like smorgasbord, is that it?" she said sharply as she stomped off to the other vegetables.

"Grab that eggplant," he commanded her happily. She picked it up and put it into the basket. "What does Nicki think about her beautiful, very sexy mother, who doesn't see any men except for an occasional doctor? Does she think that's normal?" She clamped her teeth shut in frustration, remembering her daughter's queries about dating mothers. "Well?"

"Would you rather I sleep with a group of different men . . . maybe take on the staff of a clinic or small hospital?"

"I want you to sleep with only one man—me." His voice held a threat and a promise. She blinked wide eyes at him. He seemed to be off-balance for a moment also. He must have the notion that his badge gave him the right to pick and choose women like other people gathered vegetables from the produce aisle. She wondered what line he used on Linda. "Maureen, I think we could be very good for each other." That was the line that broke the camel's back, but she would have to give him an A for the sincerity in his tone.

"You've really got nerve to proposition me when you've just climbed out of a very warm bed, Captain." Maureen was livid. "I saw her! She was sophisticated, gorgeous, and seemed quite taken with you. And don't try to tell me she was your sister."

"You'd never believe that one."

"No!" She glared at his determined face as she noticed he had finished shaving and remembered how smooth his face had felt. She looked away and down at the basket. "I don't want eggplant," she said, wondering how the vegetable got into the basket. She placed it back in the pile of other eggplants.

"I do," he said with an intimidating tone. "Isn't that what you were going to ask me earlier, to come to Thanksgiving dinner?" He flipped back his coat and jacket to jam an impatient hand into his slacks pocket. His thighs flexed against the fabric, and she tried to erase the image of the bare thigh she had seen earlier.

"You're incredible!" she fumed.

"Thank you," he said, replacing the eggplant in the basket. She rolled her blue eyes in frustration and continued to move along the aisle, but she could feel him close by.

"Would you please go away!" she breathed as she whirled and dropped an onion into the basket.

"Those tomatoes look terrific for this time of year," he said covetously, moving beyond her up the aisle, avoiding her angry glare, and dismissing her request.

"Not nearly as scrumptious as the one you had last night," she said, almost shouting, her cheeks flaming. "It seems tomatoes are never out of season for you."

"My, my. Jealous, aren't we?"

"Jealous!" she croaked. "Don't flatter yourself. I'm not jealous."

"Go ahead, you can admit it. I don't mind."

"Oooh!" she fumed, stacking handfuls of carrots and a bunch of celery into the basket and jamming in oranges too. She grabbed the basket away from her tormentor and rushed for the checkout counter. Tony followed with a brisk stride. Maureen unloaded the food for Mrs. O'Neal to tally. He was, luckily, silent at the checkout, but she could feel his brooding presence behind her. Her mind was whirling about ten thousand miles per hour as the cash register trudged through its paces. She wanted out of this store and away from Tony DiRocco.

"I didn't want those tomatoes or eggplant," she said, puzzled as to how they homed into her groceries.

"Yes, we do." He smiled politely at Mrs. O'Neal as she packed them carefully into a brown bag, surreptitiously watching and speculating about the couple at her counter. "I'll get this, darling," Tony said smoothly to Maureen, fishing his wallet from his pocket and handing some bills to the woman. Kindly Mrs.

O'Neal gave Maureen a pleased look. The woman had watched her grow from a girl into a warm, caring young woman.

"You will—" Maureen started an angry denial.

"I insist, honey," he said, smiling, but his dark eyes burned with a challenging light. Snatching up the heavy bag of produce, not even pretending to wait while he got his change, Maureen charged into the cold air and bustled up the sidewalk.

"Maureen!" he called when he was nearly a step behind.

"How dare you?" She whirled on him, her coat flapping open; she was steaming. "I've shopped in that store since I was a little girl. That dear woman thought we were lovers! You intentionally —"

"You aren't a little girl anymore, and you have too damn much fire to pass for the old maid you pretend to be. Believe me, you're not the type. That old woman was tickled pink because she thought we were lovers. And I fully intend that we will be lovers," he pledged. Her pulse skittering through her veins was a warning; she must fight him and herself. "Let me have that bag. It's too heavy for you," he said, taking it from her and walking to his car. "I'll drive you." He turned to see her tenacious form standing firm in the middle of the sidewalk. He put the groceries on the back fender of the gold car. Her hands were bunched into fists and propped on her curved hips. Her nose and cheeks were already red from the cold. She was one fierce, smoking dragon with her warm breath forming billowing clouds through her clenched teeth. He smiled and then closed the distance between them with determined strides.

"You can't believe I'm not falling for your Mediterranean charm, can you?" she said fiercely, determined to remain glued to the spot where she stood and adamant about thwarting his magnetism.

"It hasn't failed me yet." His dark eyes scanned her face as he gently tilted the tam on her shining hair, closed her plum pea coat, and tightened the pink knit scarf around her neck.

"Read my lips, Captain," she said with a slight tremor in her rising voice, "because you don't seem to hear what I'm saying. I am not falling in love with you. Not now, not ever," she lied.

"Don't worry, princess. I'm getting all your signals loud and clear. I'm not the one who's not listening!" She saw his expression tighten, the muscles flick along his jaw. She couldn't understand his persistence.

"I'm not going to swoon from your machismo and roll over on my back the way all your other women do, Antonio." Despite her anger, somehow she could not control the seductive lilt in her tone when she pronounced his name.

"You may get a whole new perspective of life while lying on your back," he accused her, not trying to bridle his temper now.

"My life . . ." she said, grabbing him by the sleeve, "my life was just fine until you came into it." Tears pushed hard at the corners of her eyes. "That's your idea to cure everything, isn't it, just hop into the sack and everything will be fine. That's just when the trouble and complications begin! Damn you!" she shouted. She had stopped dreaming of ever finding love, stopped aching and wanting until he brought Nicki home that day. "You came into my life and messed it all up." She swung a stinging hand and aimed for his chest with a wallop, slapping his trench coat. "You stay in my house!" She slammed his chest again and he did nothing to stop her or protect himself as they stood in a cloud of steam from her hard, fast breathing. "You find me late at night and say loving things to me, you pay for my groceries, you confuse me. . . ." He had been so cruel to let her dream again when he really belonged to someone else. That's why she couldn't forgive him. That's what made her so violently angry. She couldn't stop hitting him, pummeling his chest with her fists, any more than she could dam back the tears. He fished his badge out of his pocket to show the concerned shop owners and patrons watching from their windows. But she couldn't stop. "You're a cop, you're confusing . . ." She couldn't believe she was so aggressive. Maureen was crying and Tony's all too appealing face was out of focus, but she could feel his strong arms bracing her.

"You're one tough woman," he said, dodging her last high blow. "And I could arrest you for assaulting a police officer," he said, subduing her with a hug of his powerful arms. "I'm warning you, princess, once I take you in, you're mine and I'll never let you go," he vowed. "Why don't you just admit that you want me?" She shook her head in denial. "I can see it in your eyes," he said, backing her against the warm glass of the bakery window. "I can feel it when I'm close to you. Why don't you just admit it?"

"How dare you!"

"You've done nothing but lie to me and tell me half-truths since I've met you," he said, his voice deceptively soft and mellow. "It's my business to know when people are telling the truth," he answered her wide-eyed, questioning look. "Shall we have a discussion about the various reasons people lie?"

"No!" The word came out in a defensive blurt.

"Then tell me the truth. Just admit it," he whispered.

"No, I—"

"Don't you know I won't hurt you," he murmured, nuzzling her with his cold nose, his warm lips burning against her chilled skin as he tenderly kissed away the salty tears on her cheeks and from the corners of her mouth. His gentleness was killing her will.

"I could hurt you," she whispered, tears welling up and threatening to brim over again. He relaxed his hold on her as he watched two giant tears roll down her cheeks.

"Here, I can't stand to see a dame cry," he said in his best Bogie, handing her a handkerchief. She was laughing through her tears as she gratefully accepted it, dabbing at her eyes and nose. "That's what I've been trying to tell ya, sweetheart," he teased her, his dark eyes shining. "We dirty coppers are all alike—tough, see?

"Tough guy, huh?" She smiled, grateful for his humor. She felt so silly hitting him.

"I can take whatever you got to dish out, doll, both barrels." He was so close, his breath was warming her cheeks and lips, and she could see a fleeting illusion of emotion and compassion in his eyes. Had she really seen him at a vulnerable moment?

"My only weakness is getting knocked out by a gorgeous dame like you," he said, suddenly slipping back into his own husky voice, reading her mind like lines from a movie script. She couldn't deny he was special and made her feel wonderful.

"Don't talk like that," she laughed. He talked rough to her, living the philosophy of matinee idols—never lie to a woman and always giving her what she wants—love.

"Why not, sweetheart?"

101

She smiled up at him through her tears.

"It's not fair, making me laugh when I want to be so angry with you."

"Maybe you really don't want to be angry." His gaze warmed her as his eyes became a devouring, shimmering black.

"Maybe," she whispered. She admitted that Tony ranked right up there with the last of the tough guys, but it was his sweetness that was sapping her will. But she denied that she loved him. She had to. Wondering how she could resist the last of the tough guys, she was drawn to his lean, carved face. *Of all the houses in all the towns in all the world, he had to walk into hers. . . .* She smiled as she reached up tenuously to kiss his smooth cheek and to caress the corner of his mouth with warm, quivering lips.

Impatiently Tony covered her mouth with his, hungrily feasting on her parted pink lips, warming her inside and out. Pushing her against the frosty store window and pressing his sinewed thighs against her weak legs, his tongue flirted over her lips and entered, exploring the recesses of her mouth. Opening her coat, he pulled her body more fully against his and her breasts reacted to the cold and to the feel of his muscled chest. She melted against him as her seeking hands slid below his coat and jacket, feeling his radiating warmth and the muscled bands of his sides and back. She felt gloriously alive in his arms, savoring his kiss and dreaming wondrous dreams, until her shoulder and arm nudged his holster.

She stiffened and retreated for an instant, but he pulled her closer still, evidently planning to kiss her fear away. His kiss became more earnestly tender with light, relentlessly gentle caresses, inviting, entreating her to trust him, not to be afraid. Her mind wanted to resist, but her body clung to the safe harbor of his arms. Her body responded to his lovemaking and her mind floated into a long-forgotten dreamworld. She snuggled her love-starved body against his sensual feast as a tightening tugged deep inside her, reminding her of more complete celebrations. Heightened desires and longings crowded out her fear as she sighed in resignation against him, retiring from the battle wanting only to feel his skin under her hands and her body next to his. The focus of her entire universe was strung along the jagged line where her soft curves met his rugged ranginess. After an eternity he lifted his head, and they peered ponderously at each other through the cloudy fog of their own steaming passion. They were both so warm and close that their breath turned into one instant gushing cloud instead of two. She laughed at the foggy, billowing sight.

"You can't deny it, princess, so will you admit—"

"I'll admit . . . that I was going to ask you to dinner tomorrow," she said, trying to sidle out of his arms.

"That's a start," he said, slowly and reluctantly releasing her.

"Noon?" She was attempting to recover gracefully from his soul-shaking kiss.

"I'll be there." He smiled. "That's another thing I really love about you, Maureen. You're stubborn as hell." He quickly replaced the pink knit tam that tipped off her head and glanced at the smiling patrons and pastry chefs in the bakery, who were watching them through the wet circles on the frosted windows. Maureen knew that Chicagoans watched everything from muggings to gospel street bands, from stuffed ballot boxes to St. Paddy's Day parades. They put up with the Cubs, politicians, and the Bears, but they celebrated lovers. Yet Maureen blushed gravely at the sight of the appreciative audience. Tony put a protective arm around her and guided her away from the window to the waiting car. "So, when you do finally make up your stubborn mind that you love me, I'll know it'll be forever," he said, giving her shoulders a squeeze. "I'll drive you home."

She shook her head. "No, the supercop has to get to work before crime runs rampant in the streets, and I need to walk." *And think,* she neglected to say.

"Are you all right, Maureen?"

She nodded. She gathered her groceries and turned without another word, walking back up the sidewalk. She was fine until she heard his car drive away. She swallowed hard, fighting back tears. She wouldn't let it happen with him, not again, not even for beautiful dreams, she promised herself. She couldn't force Tony into the role of her knight in shining armor. The gallant knight roamed free, true only to himself and his honor. She wouldn't shackle him, not the last of the sexy tough guys. How could anyone capture an illusive dream? As she passed the bakery, its owner, Mr. Novelli, bounded from the door.

"Miss Ryan," he called after her. "This is for you," he said, stuffing a circle of freshly baked fragrant bread into her brown bag. "Ah, love, it's wonderful!" His round face beamed and his moustache sparkled with moisture collected in the cold. "He's a very nice man?"

"Yes, he is, Mr. Novelli," she said, enjoying the opportunity to be honest and delighting in his jovial laughter. "Thank you."

"I can't help it." He winked at her. "I've been married thirty-eight years and I still love romance, not like the young kids today. Now, you and your young man, that's another story." He smiled.

For a moment she enjoyed the gift of thinking of Tony as her own. "Thank you." She smiled and walked back toward her empty house on Clover Street. But tomorrow the house would be filled with life, laughter, love, and food for the holiday. She blushed, remembering the taste of love she so recently shared and enjoyed with Tony DiRocco. But she was painfully aware that she still wasn't filled and she was relegated to starvation. Yet her spirits irrationally soared. Tomorrow would be feast, and she was too excited to worry about famine.

CHAPTER SEVEN

Tony couldn't wait any longer. He wanted to see Maureen and hold her in his arms, touch her perfect skin, kiss her. He loved her and he wanted to tell her while he made love to her. But now, cooling his heels at the door, he felt uncomfortable as he looked questionably at the bottle of red wine and the twelve pink roses in his hand. Damn it! Being in love with a woman makes a man do crazy things, he decided as he slipped an index finger inside the too small space between his throat and the collar of his plaid shirt of warm shades of gold, brown, and rust held snug by a brown knit tie. If he wasn't careful, he'd be thinking about marriage soon, about a light in the window and coming home to Maureen's soft embrace. *Slow down, buddy,* he warned himself. *Besides, who'd want a broken-down old cop like you anyway?* He would worry about all that later, whether or not Maureen would even want him in her life that way. For now, he was only hungry to lay eyes on her.

He glanced down at his casual brown corduroy blazer, neat flannel slacks, and the dull sheen of his leather shoes. He always dressed carefully, wanting to look his best, yet he didn't want to wear a business suit. He wasn't on the job or going to see a casual date, a one-night stand or a what's-your-name. He was going to see the woman he loved and he craved to find her returning his look with one of desire and love. He longed for her in the most primitive way, but, also, he wanted her in the most idealistic, starry-eyed way imaginable. How could he be complete, be a real man, without a wife and family to love and care for? Everything was coming together, and Maureen was at the center of it all. Maureen was sensitive and caring, and who could refuse Nicki as a friend, ally, and daughter? Foreign but peaceful visions of home and hearth floated through his mind as he stood at the oak doors.

Tony was confident that he had won the battle of wills by waiting until nearly noon to rap on the high oak double doors that did little to stop the delicious aroma of food from filtering into his apartment since early morning.

He would give her the flowers and watch her blush pretty shades of pink to match the roses, tell her he loved her, then kiss her. God, he loved the way she flowed into his arms, so soft and warm against him, making him feel so powerful and strong. She made him forget he was even capable of deliberate and practiced lovemaking and filled him with a hot passion. He had always been a gentleman to all the women he'd taken out, holding doors for them, lighting their cigarettes, being politely and sexually attentive even when he didn't like them much. But he'd never felt that he needed to protect and cherish a woman. Maureen made him feel that way. Yet he knew she wasn't fragile or timid. His pretty little princess had a steel band of courage, intelligence, and a street toughness if she needed it. And she possessed an abundance of sexual fire behind all her retiring shyness, a fire he liked to think burned for him alone. She didn't turn on all quick and hot with lightning speed, but she hummed with a genuine tender quiet warming that could keep the love embers glowing for a lifetime.

He was schooling himself not to pull her into his arms the moment she opened the door, when he heard someone approaching. The door rolled open and Tony's smile faded as he stood peering into a lined, gaunt face crowned with thinning curly brown hair. Tony studied the man skeptically, trying to make contact with the shifting brown eyes veiled behind thick lenses.

"You must be the handsome hunk," he said blandly to Tony. For the first time in his life Antonio DiRocco was speechless. Visions of a little familylike gathering with just him and his two favorite women disappeared like smog on a rainy gray day in

Gary. Tony glanced around, scanning the rooms for Maureen and Nicki, but they weren't in sight and this joker seemed to be impervious to Tony's narrowed, stern gaze.

"You shouldn't have, really," the man whined, brashly grasping the flowers and wine from his hand.

Tony answered by giving the man the most frank, who-in-the-hell-are-you stare and a get-lost-as-soon-as-Maureen-shows-up gesture as his hands flexed at his sides. Where in hell was she? He glared through and beyond the man blocking his way into the house. This day was not going as he had planned, not at all. Tony brushed by the man and, entered the dining room.

"You know, it's really funny. You don't even look like a cop." The man gloated.

Tony nodded without a smile. He could feel the tension creeping up through his muscles into his shoulders and neck. He hadn't figured Maureen for the vengeful type. Maybe this was just her little way of telling him she didn't want any other women in his life. How could his sixth sense have led him into this ambush? he steamed quietly.

"That's all right. You don't look like an orthodontist," Tony drawled, his voice tight and course.

"Oh, God, no!" He laughed, watching Tony warily. "I'm no orthodontist! I'm an artistic genius! I'm Myron Feldman. Mo's boss," he clarified at Tony's lack of recognition. "You obviously weren't expecting anyone else here today, but I kind of come with the Thanksgiving dinner around here, kind of like dressing for the turkey, you know." Then Myron Feldman did something Tony thought impossible. He blanched even more pale at Tony's apparent lack of a sense of humor. Myron fidgeted and smiled nervously, nodding and making another attempt to be sociable. "Nicki's told me all about you." Tony sized up the man and determined this was not the dragon, not even in disguise. "Let me warn you, officer, these two girls have larceny in their souls. They can steal your heart and your money," he said disheartedly as he looked at the roses in his hand. "I'm just a friend of the family. . . . Of Maureen and Nicki's. Not *The* Family." Tony braced himself for the next five godfather jokes and was tempted to make Myron Feldman an offer of his own. The jokes never came. Myron Feldman laughed nervously and retreated.

107

"Mo! Your Italian stallion is here!" he shouted as though calling for the cavalry, and then added with chagrin, "And he brought flowers."

Nicki gave a little squeal of delight as she breezed through the swinging door from the kitchen, oohing over the bouquet and carrying a vase filled with water as though she already knew the flowers were there.

"Wow, how beautiful, Tony!" Nicki cried, collecting the roses gingerly from Myron while breathing in the fragrance of the pink buds nestled in sprays of baby's breath. "Flowers, wow!" She lifted both brows and smiled at him. Tony tugged on her curls. He was pleased to see the girl's sunshine after the disappointing reception.

"It won't be too long and you'll be getting flowers." He stood back enjoying Nicki's giggle.

"I see you've already met Myron," she said, and then added in a conspiratorial whisper that was obvious, "he's deranged, you know. He thinks he's an artist." Her eyes sparkled with a teasing light.

"Tell him I'm a friend of the family," Myron demanded.

"I've never seen him before in my life," Nicki chortled.

"A teenage con artist!" he accused Nicki, gesturing in exasperation at her. Tony was beginning to relax in the easy jibing and camaraderie. "That little monster just won a ten-dollar bet about the flowers."

"He's a gambling addict, so I try to humor him," she chuckled. "And, besides, Captain DiRocco is a very safe bet." She smiled at Tony. "Especially from the rumors I heard at the grocery store after school yesterday," she added smugly.

"I think we were both set up." He smiled and offered his hand to a relieved Myron Feldman. "Happy Thanksgiving, Myron. In case you haven't guessed, I'm Tony DiRocco. You surprised me earlier—at the door."

"I'm glad to meet you," Myron said, returning Tony's hearty handshake.

"Yes," Tony said. "I'm sorry about—"

"That's all right," Myron threw up his hands to dismiss it. "Your name is familiar though. Until now I've only heard you referred to as the hunk," he said, gesturing toward the red-faced teenager still fussing with the flowers. "Tony DiRocco?" Myron muttered, tapping his skull in thought.

"Yes. Captain Antonio DiRocco of the Twenty-Eighth Street Station, South Side," Tony rattled off automatically with a smile, now having the time to note the picture-perfect dining table with white linen cloth, glistening china and crystal, and shining silver. Things were looking much more like what he had envisioned. His eyes took in the dried flower arrangement in the center of the table and the apple pies on the sideboard. He strode to the doors and rolled them completely open so the house was one unit again. That made the scene complete. Things got off to a rocky start, but today he planned on making history. Nicki smiled and finished the flower arranging, lifting the vase for his approval. He nodded as his restless eyes swept toward the closed kitchen door.

"Mom's in the kitchen," Nicki said, possibly sensing his anticipation.

"I'll chill this," Myron waved the bottle of wine. "DiRocco? DiRocco?" Myron muttered as he walked through the swinging door of the kitchen. "I've got it!" he shouted on the other side. Before the door could swing back, Myron burst through again, still carrying the bottle of wine. "Are you *the* Tony DiRocco?" Myron asked, pointing an index finger at him. The finger was long and bony, apparently from exercising his artistic genius. But it was his wide, smiling mouth and excited discovery in his eyes that puzzled Tony.

"Yes?" Tony said hesitantly, wondering what reaction would follow.

"That's fantastic! Perfect!" He about-faced and slammed into the kitchen. Seconds later he came crashing through the door again with Maureen in tow. She was trying to discard her apron from atop her soft, sheer plum dress that gently hugged the curves of her bosom and gracefully sheathed her hips. Her hair was different today. The blond tresses were pulled back from her face and twisted into a complicated knot at the back of her neck.

"This is fantastic, Mo," her boss repeated over and over. Finally he turned her narrow shoulders to face Tony's discriminating eye. She held her yellow print apron behind her. She was beautiful. Skin like alabaster tinted with natural rose and pink lips sweetly curving into a timid smile. The deep pools of

109

azure took his mind away to a dream. *Don't lose your head, fella, just smile at the lady. Don't scare her away,* he coached himself, *you come on too strong because you want her so much. Easy. Easy.*

"Mo, this is Tony DiRocco," Myron said proudly, as if he'd made the wonderful discovery on his own.

"Yes," Maureen murmured. "We've already met." Maureen could almost say she was in control, until she looked into Tony's melancholy eyes holding hers in a dark, intense gaze. He was beautifully golden; his sensual mouth begged for a soft caress that would ignite into fire, and his tense, manly body was etched with a consuming sexual energy that at once frightened and thrilled her. Yes, they had met. She had melted from his kisses and trembled in his arms. Oh, yes, they had met before in many dreams. She was so attracted to him, it must be written all over her face and transmitted in unmistakable signs from her body. Her left hand smoothed back her hair and checked the chignon at the nape of her neck. Her cheeks burned from his flagrant appraisal. She felt like a fool, falling in love with a dream. But the Antonio DiRocco casually bracing his strong straight arms on the back of an antique chair in the pale green dining room and relentlessly observing her was very real.

"This isn't just your generic run-of-the-mill cop you've got here for dinner, Mo," Myron said skeptically, disbelieving her silence. His observations were unnecessary. "This man's a bonafide hero in Chicago. There's been articles in the *Trib* about you, right? The On the Street column. He writes about you, doesn't he?" Myron looked at Tony then to Nicki and Maureen. "You're the one, aren't you?" he asked Tony.

"I'm the one." He spoke softly and tried to catch Maureen's eye to gauge her reaction.

"Man, I don't believe this guy," Myron said. "Do you believe this guy? Ladies, may I present," Myron introduced with dramatic flare, "the Blue Knight of Chicago."

"Wow!" Nicki exclaimed with a delighted smile. "A knight!"

"He's very special," Maureen conceded, thinking aloud. Tony's features softened for a moment, analyzing her quiet statement. He was the man of her dreams; she didn't need a newspaper columnist to tell her that. He was hers in fantasies so real that she reached for him in the middle of the night only to find

110

her wide bed empty, and to ache until dawn. Myron rattled on about Tony's arrests—or "collars" as he explained the police jargon—commendations, and medals of valor.

"He always gets who he's after," Myron said finally. "Isn't that right?"

"Always," Tony agreed, his compelling regard on Maureen. The positive current flowing from the tightly coiled man was vibrating through her, initiating a sexual buzz that traveled through her body and charged her to the very core.

"Wow!" Nicki breathed.

"Do you know this guy even ran down a getaway car on foot?" Myron explained to Nicki, who looked from one romantic statue to the other. "How did you do that?"

"Wow!" Nicki repeated just above a whisper.

Somehow nothing about Antonio DiRocco surprised her, Maureen thought as she tried to break his mesmerizing spell. Perhaps he was really a sorcerer rather than a knight, or maybe he'd been charmed by a wizard in order to rescue damsels in distress. Whatever his purpose, she had to protect him and keep him safe. She smiled at her own thoughts, wondering why she thought this tough guy needed protection, but she said, "Perhaps the captain will tell us the story over dinner. I think we better get the meal on the table." She glanced at her enthralled daughter. "Nicki, would you help?"

"Sure, Mom," Nicki said, following her mother.

It was a feast that delighted both the eye and the palate. The gleaming table service and the gentle glow from the chandelier were a perfect backdrop for the masterpiece of dinner Maureen had prepared. The platters and crystal dishes held deep red cranberries, burnt umber candied yams, golden turkey, yellow corn, and saucy red juices harboring the eggplant parmigiana. It was an array of satisfying colors, shapes, textures, and aromas. Yet the meal was not only a visual and culinary delight, but a sensual feast as well, as glances and stimulating messages flowed between the man and woman who sat at opposite ends of the table. She couldn't keep her eyes from him. Could she pretend, if only for the day, he belonged here?

111

"I hope you take special notice of this dish," Nicki said, handing Tony the dish of eggplant.

"Yes, it's very good."

"It should be. Mom really fussed about it. She even called a couple of friends from work to get the recipe just right," Nicki teased. "I don't know why she didn't just ask your sister when she met her yesterday morning." Nicki gave her mother an inquiring look.

"Your sister?"

Tony smiled at Maureen's dumbfounded expression.

"Your sister?" She trekked across a plain of the past, reviewing the pleasant, attractive features of the young woman she'd seen in his apartment, trying to visualize a lineage, reconstructing a robust father, a lovely fragile mother with delicate features and large melancholy eyes.

"You said you wouldn't believe she was my sister," he shrugged.

"Tony showed me Linda's picture. She's beautiful and she has a couple of cute little kids too. Plus she is the assistant district attorney of Cook County. You know, Linda Scarpelli."

"Yes—no—" Maureen started, questioning Tony's grinning face.

"And she's quite taken with me." Tony chuckled, his eyes meeting Maureen's to gauge the effect of their private joke. "I saw them last night for dinner. Her husband, Gerald, agrees with you and he's looking forward to meeting you." He grinned like a fox who'd found the henhouse. "Linda thought you were delightful and extremely patient—for a landlord."

She should have been embarrassed by the revelation that the woman who had made her so jealous was really Tony's sister, but Maureen was so pleased Linda wasn't romantically attached to Tony that she couldn't repress a smile. But she cautioned herself again that Maureen Ryan couldn't have him even if there were no other woman. She would do what she knew was best for both of them.

Maureen let the conversation flow around her as she stole glances at Tony. He looked magnetically attractive and more at ease than she ever thought possible as he joined in the conversation, seldom lacking for words, only to take her breath away with

112

a lazy smile or capture her with a devouring look that made her feel as though she were his favorite dish of all. The conversation had covered the police department, which had an eloquent defender, Myron's films, football, and back to movies again. She noticed Tony tense again, pressing a point.

"I saw some of Maureen's sketches. They're very good. It was amazing to see the drawings framed up and in motion," Tony said.

"Our little Mo is one of the best. She's worked with me since that one was in diapers." He pointed to Nicki. "Mo even helps edit her own scenes. She's great with the action scenes, really has a knack for the movement and sensuality."

"Sensuality, eh?" Tony nodded, quickly looking down the length of the table. "Mo got a knack you say, huh?" He totally enjoyed the rising tint of her cheeks.

"She's terrific," Myron went on. Maureen was avoiding Tony's sly smile. "And those latest drawings are right on target, fabulous stuff. I was worried there for a while. But Sir Rodney has really shaped up," Myron beamed at his prodigy. "He's definitely hit-hero caliber."

Maureen fidgeted, trying to elude the surprised looks of Nicki and Tony. "Well, that's enough shoptalk for today," she said.

"I mean it, Mo. He's inspired!"

"That squirrelly blond knight?" Nicki asked, shocked, as she tried to snag Tony's eye.

"We don't want to bore anyone, Myron dear," Maureen said, favoring her boss with a tight smile.

"Haven't you seen the drawings yet?" Myron asked Nicki and Tony.

". . . Gave up on the orthodontist," Tony muttered under his breath.

"What?"

"Mo must have been working late," Tony added. "So what does this notorious dragonslayer look like?"

"Is anyone ready for dessert?" Maureen asked brightly as she tried once more to get the crew off the track.

"Tall, dark, and handsome, with brown, almost-black sparkling eyes. Right?" Nicki asked, biting her lower lip so she wouldn't smile at her mother's stricken expression.

113

"So you did see them. Actually," Myron said, squinting at Tony for a moment, "he looks a lot like—"

"Apple pie à la mode," Maureen announced, trying to smile.

"Personally, I think that Rodney is the best thing Maureen has ever done." Myron continued to ooze. At any other time she would have basked in the compliments, but now Maureen cringed when he added, "And those scars were a touch of genius."

"Scars?" Tony asked innocently, his interest piqued as he scanned her with a warm regard that Maureen dared not meet.

"What knight is believable without a few battle wounds, right?"

"Right," Nicki agreed.

"Just a few on his arms and a sexy one on his side," Myron listed.

"Sexy!" Nicki said, rolling her eyes and then looking at Tony, who caught but discreetly dodged her inquiring look. The situation was out of Maureen's control, and she felt overcome with heat.

"I'll get the dessert," Maureen said stiffly as she got up from the table.

"A sexy scar on the side, huh?" Tony asked, watching her march from the room. "Must be artistic license," he said, but she could hear the smile in his voice.

"Oooh!" she said as she slammed through the swinging door to pace the kitchen floor.

"No one does a better fight scene than Mo," Myron agreed. "Though all her scenes reek with a sensual quality."

"I noticed that," Tony concurred. She heard his tenor voice crooning the tale.

"I didn't know you were into art, Tony?"

"Er . . . ever since I met Maureen," he said sardonically. "I don't know much about it, but I do know what I like," he added by way of explanation.

"Oooh!" Maureen fumed, grabbing the countertop to steady herself. The evolution of her knight into an Antonio DiRocco lookalike had been a slow, unconscious process until yesterday. Then she gave up fighting it and finished him off in one afternoon —dark, gold, and handsome with long, sad eyes that could flash

114

from fierce to loving in an instant. Maureen stomped around the kitchen, slamming drawers and cabinets in her wake. She only regretted she couldn't draw the sound of his voice, but now she couldn't stand his arrogant teasing. He knew she couldn't resist him.

"It sounds like your mother is having trouble with the ice cream," Tony said calmly. "You sit still, honey. I'll help her," he said confidently to Nicki.

Maureen heard him push through the swinging door but she refused to face him. She continued to grip the counter.

"I brought the pies," he said. "You cut and I'll dip the ice cream," he said loudly. He walked to the counter where she stood and placed a pie on either side of her, resting his hands on the counter also. He bent his head, caressing the hollow below her ear with a warm whisper that promised more. She closed her eyes, tuning out the beckoning.

"No, don't!" she said, turning to face him but still clutching the counter behind her as security. She couldn't allow herself to follow her feelings. Damn it. He was so sure that she was in love with him. He was right. So much for the woman of mystery!

"Oh, I insist," he said lazily. "It's the least I could do." He perused her frame with obvious appetite.

She started to speak, but Tony covered her mouth with a possessive kiss, whose full power she avoided by turning her head. "So you gave up on your orthodontist," he whispered against her warm mouth.

"I didn't say that," Maureen whispered angrily, trying to shrink away from him, but her breast still brushed erotically against his chest.

"I did." He gave her a firm, proprietorial scan, then breathed out a steady stream of frustration. "Don't fight me, Maureen."

"The drawings don't mean what you think," she said haughtily.

"Are you trying to tell me you didn't borrow my body for your inspired knight?" He breathed against her cheek. She was trying to concentrate on the voices of Nicki and Myron in the next room instead of on the romantic tones near her ear. His warm, titillating breath was on her temple and the disturbing recollected images of the golden body so close to hers, nearly naked, erupted in her mind.

"Yes." She lied in a hiss. Her breath was coming in erratic spurts as she reminded herself that she couldn't allow him to become ensnared by an illusion of the happiness they could never share.

"I don't believe you, princess." The rasp of the sultry, reedy quality hummed through his tone and vibrated through her middle. Her drawings weren't entirely innocent. She reasoned that if she couldn't have him herself, she would capture him with pen and ink. She wanted to keep him forever, but it would only hurt both of them. His breathing was shallow and warm against her skin as his lips cruised along her cheek. She could hear his hands harshly gripping the counter beside her hips and she tipped her head to the side as he nibbled on her ear.

"Tony, please—"

"I think it's only fair that if you use my body, we strike a fair trade. You have terrific bargaining material here," he murmured against her arched velvet throat. "Damn it, I've wanted to do this for hours!" He groaned quietly, pulling her tender body into his arms, kissing her full warm lips hungrily, as though he were a starving man. She relished his desire. It was a glorious, heady feeling, but she couldn't bear the thought of him being disappointed in her, like a child who excitedly unwraps a Christmas present only to be disappointed by the contents. His sexual intensity frightened her and excited her. His hand slid over the fabric of her dress so lightly, she almost decided she wanted him, until she felt the warmth of his palm just below the curve of her breast. Could she pretend that she could satisfy him? But what would happen when he realized the truth?

"You're a delicious dessert," he whispered huskily, nuzzling her neck, nibbling her satiny skin, flicking his tongue provocatively on her throat. She couldn't hurt him.

"Antonio . . ." She sighed before she was swept away on the wings of another heated caress. She couldn't help herself as she relaxed against his powerful form. Her knight surrounded her with strong, muscled bands that could have squeezed her very life away, but he held her passionately, sweetly, kissing her. Maybe she could dream. She returned his tenderness as her arms

116

Austin with its large houses and comfortable bungalows. He felt as far away from Maureen as he had from the untouchable St. Ursula girls so many years ago at the bus stop. He looked at the girl beside him, wondering about the original motive for inviting him to look at their apartment only a few weeks ago. Could his whole life change in a few weeks? His mind refused to answer.

"So, how are you and what's his name getting along?" he asked, trying to change the subject. She didn't reply. "You know, the lucky guy who likes to tease you? Did you ask him to walk you home?"

"No!" The simplicity of her reply held a world of frustration.

"Why not?"

"What if he didn't like me? He might laugh at me or think I have ugly braces and—"

"Of course he'll like you. I'm only worried he'll like you too much. You're gorgeous, just like your mother!" He gestured with his left hand, keeping his right steadily on the steering wheel.

"Hmmm."

"Hmmm? What's that mean?" he asked irritably. "You even talk like your mother." Nicki's lack of confidence was phenomenally unnecessary and a constant source of wonder. "You're a lovely young lady, Nicole. I'm sure Danny has noticed that. You're sweet, honest, intelligent—"

"A great personality, right? That's the kiss of death," she said sarcastically. "But you sound like a father." She giggled.

"Yeah, well . . ." He nodded, glancing at her. "It's an occupational hazard."

"No, it's not," she said sweetly. "So?" She didn't evoke a reply. "So are you in love with my mother? Would you like to marry her?" she asked bluntly. Her eyes were shining with a pleasant emotion and hope.

"Nicki," he started, "don't count on me being the knight in shining armor that sweeps your mom off her feet." No matter how much he would like to be, she still resisted him.

"But . . ."

"This isn't a fairy tale, kiddo," he said shortly.

"Do you love her?"

"I know you do," he said emphatically. He tried to convince

circled his neck, finding the fine soft hair at his nape above his collar with caressing fingers. Yes, she could pretend nothing harmful would come their way. His tongue flirted with her lips, teasing, parting them until it met its playful mate for a blissful frolic. The kiss deepened, entwining their tongues as eager partners for a slow, sensual dance. He was part of her, and she wanted him closer; she pulled his head down to hers, drinking in his energy, charging her spirit and body with an urgent longing. Suddenly there were no dragons, no fears. Just her knight loving her and she loving him. She pressed her body into his solid strength, hungrily wanting more.

"Do you two need any help out there?" Myron called from the dining room. The intruding voice jarred her back to reality, back to her fears. She lay her head on his shoulder, listening to her own panting and the beat of his heart coming in rapid thuds.

"Antonio, please," Maureen whispered when his head bent down again to capture her tender, quivering lips. She was trembling in his arms, afraid of her own passions, but undeniably wanting more of him, always more.

"A fair trade, princess," he charged her quickly, and promised. "I'll see you later—alone. You'll be all mine."

She couldn't trust her voice to protest his bold assumption. How could she, when her body responded so completely and willingly to his touch? Hadn't her desperate survivor's sense known from the beginning? How could anything that felt like such a lovely heavensent dream bring harm to the man she loved? She took the risk of looking directly into his eyes. The love and desire she saw there were so sincere, boiling in a dark liquid caldron of passion, it startled her. She was afraid she would never satisfy. . . .

"Later . . ." he whispered.

"Do you want me to help serve, Mom?" Nicki called.

"Yes, Nicki," she returned, swallowing hard, staring wide-eyed at the smiling eyes before her. Tony released Maureen abruptly as he heard Nicki bump into the kitchen door.

She was safe from his charms for a while longer, but what would happen later? Alone with a dream that so easily overwhelmed her, she wouldn't have a chance or the will to resist his insistent kisses. She wanted him so; she didn't want to resist.

Maybe she could have him for a little while. She wouldn't expect a commitment, not from a swaggering knight who would be here today and off to other lands tomorrow for new adventures. *God, listen to yourself! You know you couldn't stand to lose him. Don't set yourself up for heartbreak, you fool. Protect yourself, survivor! That's how you've made it this long. Stop it now, while you are both still in one piece.*

It would have been funny if he weren't so frustrated. Tony looked at his watch again, snapped the gold case closed, and returned it to his pocket. And then he glanced down at his armies that were about to conquer Europe. Maureen creatively invented ways of making sure she was never alone with Tony for the rest of the afternoon. The dishes were finished, the football games analyzed, coffee was served, and, finally Maureen and Myron settled down behind her drawing table to check out some sketches. Tony fantasized for a moment about being able to sit and watch Maureen draw for the next forty years or so, while Nicki was taking her turn at the board game that she and Tony chose to play. But now, as he watched Maureen's shapely legs beneath the table and saw the sheer, plum-colored material of her dress slide up her thighs when she crossed one slender leg over the other, he was going crazy.

Myron leaned close to her, laughing, and Tony decided he couldn't really tolerate another man—not even a friend of the family—near her for any reason. He was going to make a fool of himself very soon if Myron didn't ease off.

"Hey, kid!" Tony spoke more loudly than he had wanted, the frustration evident in his voice. Nicki turned her questioning face up and Maureen paused from her shoptalk with her lips pursed in triumph. God, how he wanted to kiss those pouting lips. "Would you like to go to a movie?" he asked, tearing his gaze from Maureen and turning to the savvy teenager.

"Sure," she agreed, smiling. "We can just leave these two to talk shop and we'll go and enjoy ourselves." Nicki got up from their game of Risk. Antonio the Greek and his armies had conquered several continents and was threatening western Europe on the game board, and still the lovely Princess Maureen eluded

and defied him. But suddenly it wasn't a game anymore. up, restless and prowling.

"There's a Rocky movie on at the Cinema," she said.

"One, two, three, or six?" he asked vacantly.

"Does it matter?"

"No," he said flatly. Nicki smiled knowingly. "I'll go sta car." He nodded a farewell to the two at the table. As he through the archway into his apartment to get his keys there still something tugging at him that made it impossible for to close the door. He shed his jacket, slipped on his holster gun, collected his badge and the electronic signal that he al carried when he was away from a phone. He didn't bother to on a coat; he just steamed as he charged out the door. It was t to leave the enchanted land of Maureen Ryan and get back the real world.

He had turned over a new leaf in his life all right; he allowed someone to reach through the tough walls that he so carefully constructed around himself over the years, and now he felt cruelly exposed by a woman who apparently didn't want him. But, then, why did her body beg for his attention? Bodies don't lie. He knew that from the street. Body language you could trust. Watch the hands, the shoulders, the hips, if you wanted to know what was going on inside the mind. They never lied. A smile, words, even eyes could be trained to lie, but the body had to follow the messages from the brain. Watch the body—that was his rule and his sixth sense was never wrong. And it was a pleasure to watch the body of Maureen Ryan, but he would much rather hold her. That's why he was going crazy.

Nicki slipped into the car and closed the door. She kept h dainty hands folded carefully in her lap as he backed the car o of the drive and started up the residential street.

"You two are better than the movies," she said at last, looki out the window as though she were seeing the sights for the fi time.

"What was that?" Tony asked, distracted.

"Tracy and Hepburn, Bogie and Bacall—they don't have a thing over you two. I mean . . . it's really something."

Tony groaned. "You watch too much TV, Nicki love," he looking straight ahead. The car rolled easily along the stree

himself that he didn't really love Maureen, but he was doing a lousy job.

"I don't want her to be lonely anymore," Nicki said. "I'm going to be going off to school in a few more years and I'm spending more time with my friends now. She needs someone. She needs you."

"Nicki . . ." Her perception startled him.

"I'm all she's got and I'm not enough," she said. "I know that."

"You're too young to worry about things like that." But Tony wasn't belittling her fear and concern.

"No, I'm not."

"No, you're not," he agreed, glimpsing her face, his instant affection for her becoming ever more permanent.

"She needs you," she repeated. "Before my father died she visited the hospital two or three days a week, but now . . ."

"Hey. Your mom is a lot stronger than you think," he said, reaching across the car and flicking her cheek with his finger. "Believe me, she's a fighter." They rode silently for a moment. He wondered what hold Kevin Ryan still had on the lovely princess, even from his grave. "Maybe she doesn't want any interruptions in her life. Okay?" More and more he was beginning to think she wouldn't tolerate any substitutions for her husband.

"Maybe." Her answer was low.

"I'm sorry," he said. He wasn't used to all this emotion so close to the surface. It was Maureen's fault for making him feel this way . . . so vulnerable. Sometimes she made him feel strong enough to move mountains and, at other times, as if he couldn't fight his way out of a paper bag. But he was mostly sorry that a relationship with Maureen Ryan might be impossible even though he could feel her body come to life in his arms and feel his own strength grow when he held her.

"Sometimes love isn't enough," he mumbled. Love was supposed to conquer all. That was the bill of goods he bought when he fell for Maureen Ryan. He'd been acting absolutely dazed since he'd met the woman and he'd lost all his symptoms of old age; she'd cured that completely. Now he was bringing her flowers, kissing her on the street, and thinking about her at work.

121

Tony drove past the bakery and O'Neal's Market, motoring a few more blocks to the Cinema. He was starting a new life, and he wanted Maureen Ryan to be part of it—to be all of it.

He couldn't leave out the young lady at his side as he guided her paternally through the patrons in the Cinema lobby. There were a lot of kids, a few couples, and a lot of single people.

"He's here," Nicki whispered suddenly, pulling on Tony's jacket as he slipped his change from the tickets into the pocket of his slacks. Tony quickly glanced in the direction her eyes traveled until he spotted a tall, thin, dark-eyed Casanova who couldn't keep his eyes off the young lady who blushed prettily at Tony's side and tried to hide behind her chaperone.

"You were trying to tell me this fella wouldn't be interested in talking with you," he said, arching a brow and stepping between the lovestruck teenagers, blocking their line of sight.

"Well, do you think he likes me?" He studied her skeptically but judged her sincerely naive. He hoped only that he wasn't as obvious as this adolescent Romeo when he looked at Maureen.

"Does a fish swim?" he queried ironically as he steered her past the ticket-taker into the theater.

"Nicki! What are you doing here?" It was a duet as two girls edged up to her.

"Hi! Carla, Amy! This is Tony. He's a friend of my mother's." Nicki introduced them proudly, noting her young friends' curious and admiring stares. Both girls murmured a greeting to Tony, and he smiled.

"Young ladies," he nodded, and they giggled. He politely looked away when he sensed the girls had more important matters to discuss.

"Nicki, did you see him? Danny's here and he knows you're here." Carla nudged her teasingly. Nicki's reply was a shrug and blush. "He came with our brothers and us," Carla indicated.

"Could we sit with you?" Amy asked. "We don't want to be stuck with our brothers!" she added, making a face.

"No, I don't mind," Tony laughed. "Do you need a lift home after the movie?"

"No, my mom is going to pick us up," Carla volunteered as they moved into their seats.

Danny and his friends filed in behind them a few rows back.

122

The theater darkened, music began, and the flickering images progressed through the perils of Rocky and Adrian. The saga continued. Rocky was again an unconquerable spirit and Adrian was loved and desired. It was during the training for "big fight" that an irritating electronic beep emanated from Tony's pocket.

"I've got to make a phone call, kiddo. Just wait here a minute," he whispered before he exited into the light of the lobby.

Tony was just hanging up the phone in the lobby when Nicki touched his sleeve. He hadn't decided what to do with his charge yet.

"Is everything all right?"

"No. I've got to go to work," he said, watching the girl who was becoming an increasingly important part of his life.

"Don't worry. I'll just walk home."

"Absolutely *not.*" He glanced at his watch as the solution to his predicament walked through the door into the lobby. "Wait here a moment. Okay?" He gave her a measuring look. "I just hope I'm not letting the wolf in with the lamb," he said. He purposefully walked over to Danny, who was watching them both while pretending to buy candy.

In a few moments it was arranged that Nicki would catch a ride home with Danny, Carla, and Carla's brothers.

"And you can walk her to her door," Tony added for good measure. "I want her safe, understand?" he added sternly. "That also means from you."

"Yes, sir."

Tony wondered if Danny had heard a word after he understood that he and Nicki would actually ride home together.

God, young love was so painful, but falling in love at forty wasn't all it was cracked up to be either. "Carla's mom will take you all home." Tony looked at Danny with a man's understanding. "And Danny will walk you safely to your door."

"Thank you," Nicki said, reaching up on tiptoe to kiss Tony's cheek.

"Give your mother my regrets, okay? Tell her I'll see her later," he said, backing away from them toward the exit. "Be careful going home, sweetheart."

"Okay." She smiled and Tony didn't have to ask what she was thinking. Tony nodded at her, wondering how he could really give up on Maureen Ryan. He stepped into the cold November chill. It was Thanksgiving Day, the beginning of the holiday insanity, and he was on his way to the scene of a crime. What a way to return to reality.

CHAPTER EIGHT

It was lonely and dark in Maureen Ryan's bedroom with only the reflected streetlight filtering past the filmy drapes. She had been dreaming, a nightmare. She sat up and turned to look at the illuminated hands of her alarm clock. She'd slept only an hour. Quietly lying back, she listened to her heartbeat slow down and to the sounds of the old familiar murmuring in the night. She could hear Nicki breathing in the room down the hall, and somehow she could sense Tony hadn't returned home. It was a mystery she was almost afraid to explore. Was it because she was used to listening to his sleeping sounds in the bedroom below her own, or was it mere intuition? She knew he wasn't there, and a chill caused her to pull the blankets up to her chin to gain warmth from her wide bed.

For a moment she wondered what it would be like to listen to a man sleeping in the same room, in the same bed. That was a pleasure Kevin Ryan had robbed her of. When they were married, he seldom slept with her. Instead, he spent most of his time carousing with the "boys." Since he was determined not to be saddled with a pregnant wife, he made it a point to stay out often. When he did demand his conjugal rights as her husband, he was drunk. So he fell onto her, then rolled off in a drunken stupor of unconsciousness, not sleep. He never forgave her for tricking him into marriage, although she always figured the joke was on her. After all, it was she who stopped her education to raise their child. It was Kevin Ryan's own chauvinistic idea to stop his football career and school to join the army to teach his radical wife a severe lesson.

Her eyes were wide open now, and there was no shutting them any more than she could turn off the thoughts flashing through her mind. What tragedies required a police captain on Thanksgiving evening? She couldn't erase the image of all his scars—souvenirs of past battles. Where was Tony? For years she had tuned out news stories about the Chicago police, and now her mind zeroed in on them like sonar whenever there was an announcement on TV or radio or an article in the paper. Policemen were injured or killed nearly every week in Chicago.

What was he doing?

Was he all right?

What kind of danger waited for him out there?

She had been happy to hear his voice on the phone earlier in the evening, but in the darkness she needed reassurances again. Would he come back after he was finished, or would he go somewhere else, to someone else? She aggravated him so this afternoon when she created excuses not to be alone with him; now she wished he were with her. He sounded so concerned when he called to see if Nicki and her friend made it back to the house. He was notably relieved when she assured him they were safe.

"Danny is very nice. Nicki explained about your emergency. It was very sweet of you to take the time to make arrangements for her. . . ." She paused in his tense silence. "I—I didn't have a chance to thank you for the flowers you brought today. They're very lovely. Thank you." He still didn't speak, and she was alarmed. She hesitated, listening to his breathing.

"You're welcome, princess," he said. His voice sounded less strained, almost mellow. She could hear the familiar roughness in his tone and wondered if he had any idea what just hearing his voice did to her. The longing that was tugging deep in her middle caused her cheeks to tint. "I bet you're blushing the color of those roses about now," he said.

"You're right." She laughed. "Tony, thank you."

"You know it's not hard to want to take care of Nicki and

126

. . . and I enjoyed dinner today—very much." He paused. "I warned Danny not to get fresh with Nicki."

Her giggle was musical. "I think it must have been a very effective warning. When I found them talking on the front step they were nearly frozen to death, but they were discoursing on the long-term effects of weightlessness on space travelers. They both had stars in their eyes though." She hesitated.

"You're a soft touch, Mom."

"Hmmm. Maybe so," she retorted with a soft laugh. "Will you be home soon?" The question came out so naturally, she was hoping its presumptuous innuendo would bypass the busy police captain. But it didn't.

"Believe me, I'd love to be home with you right now," he said smoothly, warming her. "I'll be home as soon as I can." Her stomach curled in pleasant anticipation. "Promise," he finished.

She was thinking much too much about Tony. He was a disturbing man that knew more than he should about her. He understood what she was thinking and feeling even before she did. She didn't know how he knew so much about her, but he was aware that she loved him. But could she show her love without destroying them both? Hadn't she already ruined and destroyed one man's life?

When she had met Kevin at Illinois State he was a jock who majored in beer blast fraternity parties and football. She met him at an antiwar demonstration late in May 1967, when she and a group of fellow protesters were sitting in the route of a ROTC parade on the college green. It was a sparkling, sunny afternoon in Champaign, lazy and lovely. Before the dress parade began, a huddle of the "fighting Illini" swarmed into the protesters with a flurry of cherry bombs and football chants, pulling long hair and beards, letting her body as heavy as possible and covering her head, when she was swept up and carried off by a big blond brute named Kevin Ryan.

"You don't belong in this battle, babe. Don't worry, I'll save you," he had told her confidently, his smile and tan cultivated to perfection. Feeling the play of muscles in his arms and back and seeing how effortlessly he carried her, she was quite certain that he could protect her. He was beautiful, Adonis-shaped, and

127

she could imagine him playing catch on the manicured lawns in front of the fraternity house. Golden and bare, except for a low-riding pair of cutoffs, she had no idea why he chose her, so she just assumed their meeting had been destiny.

He was gorgeous, muscular, bigger than life, and he came charging into her life just as she always knew the right man would, and carried her off. Perhaps not into the sunset, but into the university Union for a Coke. He stole her heart the same day as he smiled and talked above the campus chatter and the rattling ice in the paper cups of soft drinks. He was too good to be true. Or so she thought then. He never pretended to understand her political motives, but he nodded and appreciated her skimpy tank top, hip-hugging jeans, and leather sandals. And the remainder of the spring quarter they talked, swam, drank beer, went to parties, and fell into each other's arms with the eagerness of young love, as though they'd discovered something completely new, completely all their own. They had wonderful, perfect days and warm, exciting nights, he, the gridiron hero, and she, the blue-eyed blonde who talked politics and art—a real renaissance woman—giving her lectures to anyone at a fraternity party who would listen.

The dream faded over the summer, however, as reality began to grow inside her. The fall quarter let her see her hero only from a distance, galloping over the field, because he was too busy with football games and practice and coaching sessions to see her. Kevin lost his dream-come-true status when he tried to break off their relationship by telling her he thought they were getting too serious. She definitely agreed. Football was his only concern, and he shrugged it all off as just one of those things, just a spring romance. Her perfect dream of a prince turned back into a fullback frog. The most popular couple on campus suddenly transformed back into a crazy radical and a jock. How could they have changed so much?

They didn't see each other again except by accident on campus. Maureen was determined that all her energy would shift from world peace and Prince Charmings and the welfare of mankind to the microcosm growing within her and getting bigger by the day. She searched everywhere for a job to support herself and her offspring, until finally an intuitive, kind art director at a struggling movie studio hired her. She was determined to make it on her own as she couldn't bear the idea of confiding in her parents. Finally, only to ease their anxiety, she admitted who the father was. Relieved, they hustled into action. Her marriage to Kevin was a mistake and a terrible sort of blackmail that only parents can get away with. Kevin refused to take any responsibility for the baby or his new wife. He felt shackled, trapped; his dream of the pros was going down the drain because of a wife and a baby on the way. Maureen did what she could to humor him, to make it work, but she knew it was doomed from the start. If ever they seemed in opposition—with different ways of seeing the world around them, different feelings, different values—their polarity intensified only more after their marriage. How had they come together at all? Maureen sometimes wondered. She'd been blinded by love, or a dream of love. Without the nurturing love it needed for survival, their marriage died of benign neglect. Like an infant who has never been cuddled, it failed to thrive, withering on the vine even before Kevin went to Vietnam.

Maureen got up and slipped into her robe, tying the cranberry-colored satiny wrapper at the waist, covering her carnation-pink nightgown. She switched on the table lamp beside her bed, and decided to go downstairs to draw, so she went to her dresser and smoothed back her long loose tide of hair with her brush, restraining it with a ribbon.

The harsh light above the drawing table caused her to blink as the dark, handsome Sir Rodney looked back at her and she knew she must think of other things. She settled down to work, concentrating on a detailed drawing of Sir Rodney's sword and shield. She needed several different perspectives of the weapons to use as overlays and to edit in with the cels of the battle she had shown Tony a couple of weeks before. Stippled dots and tiny lines darkened and textured some areas, so that other areas took on a reflective quality as she shaded in the spaces between the filigreed patterns of the trusty shield.

She remembered Tony DiRocco's badge shining in the waning sunlight the first day she met him. It seemed like years ago, endless dreams ago. The man had been in her life only a few weeks, and he crowded her thoughts and her dreams. She poured all the effort she could into her drawing, shutting out the images of the man's smile and darting, all-seeing eyes. How did he know so much about her?

She could feel the physical relief, the tight knot in her chest giving way as she heard the now familiar sound of the gold Dodge pulling into the drive and the back door of the apartment open with a creak. The house was very quiet. She wondered anew what had called a police captain out on Thanksgiving night and kept him so late. But thank God he'd returned home.

A knock on the dining room door startled her. She crossed through the archway and around the end of the walnut table, her quickly moving robe whispering an urgent message. But she hesitated for a moment at the door.

"Maureen, is Nicki all right?" he asked through the locked door. She released the lock and rolled the door open. "I saw your light. Is everything . . . ?" He hesitated, but his visual survey flowed over her face and down her graceful throat and shoulders. It trailed over the softly glimmering fabric of her shawl-collared robe, taking in the lace of her nightgown, the color of old-fashioned sweet-scented roses, and an intriguing glimpse of cleavage. The belt cinched around her waist emphasized the pleasant swell of her breasts and the curves of her rounded hips. For a moment his sweeping regard took her breath away.

"She's fine. She's asleep." She smiled briefly. He already knew that from his call. "Are you all right? Was there trouble?" She felt simple-minded for not knowing what to ask. His silence was uncharacteristic but not frightening or uncomfortable. "Tony? Are you all right?"

"I'm feeling better by the minute," he said, his eyes starting their unhurried journey over her hills and valleys once again. "Were you drawing?" he asked, curiously tipping his head to see how she fastened her hair.

"Yes. . . . When I can't sleep I work." She most certainly felt safer with a policeman around the house, but now that he was here, her heart was in danger. "But it's getting very late. . . ." She couldn't think of anything to say.

"Please, don't shut it," he requested, putting a restraining hand on the door and rolling it open farther. "I enjoyed the door being open today—very much."

130

"Sometimes when I can't sleep I draw," she repeated, trying to start her mind working again, like priming a pump.

"Some nights when I do work I can't sleep," he said.

"We make quite a pair, don't we?" She laughed nervously.

"I think so," he said intently, without a trace of humor.

"Would you like a glass of wine?" she inquired, clearing her throat. "You brought a lovely bottle today and we haven't opened it yet." He nodded and she turned to get it from the kitchen.

"Will you have a drink with me?"

Her robe swirled and sighed about her bare feet as she stopped an instant and peered over her shoulder at his pleading eyes.

"Yes." She smiled, asking herself why she was doing such a dangerous thing. But her question was answered when she saw his features soften and some of the tension fade from his shoulders.

She returned to the open door with two stemmed wineglasses and the bottle of a fine Italian rosé, and stepped into the morning room. Tony was sitting perfectly still on the couch. Inactivity looked so foreign on him; she was so accustomed to his usual vitality and animation. She took advantage of the moment to study the belongings of the man—his paintings, his photographs —and scanned the shelves of books and records. She felt strange, since she'd never been in a man's apartment before. Kevin Ryan had been merely a transient guest in her apartment. The only things he had moved in were a couple of football trophies, his varsity jacket, and a few other articles of clothing. Then her eyes journeyed back to the tired policeman, and she studied the man himself. He leaned his head on the back of the sofa, his eyes closed and the corners of his mouth heavy, but his chin held its determined line. His long lashes fluttered open and his face came alive again, sad at first, then his eyes brightened and he smiled as he focused on her.

"You could put the wine on the table," he said, discovering her in the center of the room clutching the bottle and goblets to her bosom.

"If you're tired, I could . . ." she started, motioning toward the door.

"No!" he insisted, rising and crossing the room to take the

bottle and glasses in one hand and guide her to the couch with the other. He poured the wine and watched her sit down on the massive piece of furniture. He abruptly shrugged off his corduroy jacket and dropped it onto a chair, answering her surveying gaze. "I'll take this thing off," he said. "I don't want to frighten you." He slipped out of the leather harness and wrapped the strapping under the holster. "I'll put it over here, okay?" He asked the question rhetorically as he walked across the room to place it on the mantel.

"Why . . . why do you get called out on Thanksgiving evening?"

He set the creaking leather and heavy blue steel on the oak mantel.

"It can be anytime," he said, not turning around. He took a match from the mantel and lit the gas flames of the fireplace. "It can be anytime. It's routine to call the captain when there's been a homicide or a policeman discharges his weapon. When it's my district, I'm called." He was watching the flames for a moment. "It sounds ludicrous to talk about a routine shooting." He glanced over his shoulder to check her response. She attempted to look calm and serene, but she guessed his radar could pick up her panicked heartbeat when he turned back to the flames. "A shooting or homicide usually means a long investigation, involvement with the press, possibly more crimes related to it. The captain has to be there at the start to decide the direction and focus of the investigation, possibly to act as liaison to the media, and for later court action." Apparently she was so quiet, he turned to see if she was still there. He nearly smiled when he caught sight of her.

"This is a fairly new job for me," he said apologetically. "I've been a detective for most of my career. That was the best. I could use my head, catch the bad guys, and get them off the street." He shrugged his shoulders. "They did something wrong, they did their time. Simple." He tugged at the knot of his brown knit tie with jerky movements. Maureen didn't know the cause, but she knew Tony DiRocco was hurting and she wanted to comfort him. Had she ever really felt that way about a man before? Even when Kevin Ryan lay in the VA hospital she wanted to comfort him out of empathy and guilt, but not from love. Compassion and pity, but not love.

"I started out to be a lawyer," he said, still tugging on the stubborn tie. She tipped her head, watching him; she could picture him as a lawyer, a very impatient one.

"My father wanted me to go into the business with him. He was an excellent criminal defense attorney. God, he was good in the courtroom. He was Clarence Darrow, Perry Mason, and F. Lee Bailey all rolled into one." He soaked in her smile. "I was a third-year law student when I gave it up. I couldn't stand all the gray areas—the loopholes, the technicalities of the trial and arrest that could get criminals off the hook. I couldn't stand the thought of getting someone off that was really guilty. I mean I could rationalize that they had the right to a trial and due process and all. But what if someone I defended got off and committed another crime, created another victim. I couldn't intellectualize that." His gesture of frustration was the most spontaneous movement of the night—was he reviving? "So I went into law enforcement instead. Everything seemed so much more clear-cut and just you-break-the-law-you-pay." He stood watching the blue and green flames attempting to devour the stack of bogus logs but getting nowhere. "Beating windmills," he muttered.

Maureen carried two glasses of wine to the fireplace and set them on the mantel.

"Antonio?" She spoke softly, touching his elbow lightly. She wasn't prepared for how handsome he looked in the firelight when he turned to face her. She drew in a quick breath as she noted the play of light and shadows on his golden face, displaying prominent, chiseled planes and angles. His brilliant, saintly eyes glowed, his rough beard surrounding the straight firm line of his mouth adding sensual texture. She wanted to touch the corners of his mouth to soften the curve of his lower lip. But, instead, she loosened the recalcitrant knot in the beleaguered tie, pulling it free of his neck and releasing the button of his collar. She handed him his glass of wine as he unfastened another button.

"Thank you." His gaze never wavered from her.

"You're welcome," she said, saluting him with her glass of red

133

wine. They toasted together, looking at each other over the rims of the goblets. He reached his hand toward her as he placed his glass down, and she shied away.

"I won't hurt you," he whispered, his brow creasing for a moment with a crushed expression. His hand reluctantly bypassed her smooth, creamy cheek and pulled one end of the ribbon holding her hair. The silky tresses celebrated their freedom, cascading in a silvery sheen over her shoulders. He used both hands to gently arrange her hair in an ashen torrent. It flowed over her shoulders and breasts as though he had planned this occasion a hundred times in his mind. "You're the most beautiful schoolmarm I've ever seen," he said gruffly, swallowing hard before he moved past her to sit on the sofa.

"Tony . . . I . . . You . . ." Her heart was pounding so loudly, it blocked her ears. She wanted to comfort him, yet he was much stronger than she. She wanted to confront him, yet she dreamed of her surrender. She knew he was a man capable of violence, yet it was his tenderness that could bring her trembling to her knees. He frightened her, yet she also knew in her heart she would be completely safe only in his arms. He was the knight that could save her from the memories of the past and the dragons of her dreams.

He sat in stony silence on the couch as Maureen paced before the fireplace.

"I can't be part of your dream, Captain," she started to say firmly, almost angry that she couldn't control her own fantasies. "I stopped dreaming long ago," she admitted, looking at him through lowered lashes. In her heart she knew her words were false.

"I don't believe that."

"I refuse to be hurt again. I thought I knew the hero of my dreams once before, but he wasn't who I thought he was at all."

"You took a chance, princess. Everybody has to take a chance."

"I gambled my heart and, as it turned out, also my own little baby." Tony looked up at her incredulously, as though he were actually surprised by that detail of her life. "Nicki was born only a couple months after Kevin and I were married."

"Why . . . I mean . . ."

134

"Let's just say our marriage wasn't made in heaven." She turned away from him. "We gambled and we all lost—Nicki, I, and Kevin." She couldn't forget her feelings of betrayal, how cruelly she awakened, discovering that she wasn't in love and the man of her dreams didn't love her. A very rude awakening. What if the same thing would happen again? She and Tony were so different. What if Tony would wake up one day and realize he didn't want her. "We were angry at ourselves, our parents, each other. I participated in a peace demonstration in 1968 half from conviction and partly from hurt, neglect, and a feeling of failure."

"What did the riot—"

"My arrest stained my husband's honor so much that he thought he would teach his silly little wife a lesson by enlisting and going to Vietnam." She paused, looking up at the ceiling. "They were on a search-and-destroy mission in the Tay Ninh province. But he got partially destroyed first by friendly fire. He was never able to leave the VA hospital, but he was one damn tough Irishman. He survived two months there before an infection got him. Boy, did he ever teach me a lesson." She swallowed, her eyes moist, but she held the tears back. "He taught me not to count on dreams, Tony. It's a lot safer that way." She shook her head and walked toward him.

He caught her hand and pulled her gently down onto the couch, and she sat weakly beside him.

"I'm sor—"

"Please, don't say it." She put a finger to his lips. "It's not your fault and I've been treating you as if it were. I owe you an apology. I've been so rude to you."

"I'm a tough guy, lady. Did you forget?" he said, nearly choking on the words while the smile in his eyes withered before it reached his mouth.

"Tell me." Her eyes were glistening with unshed tears. "I don't even know what to say or what to ask. I know you're upset. Tell me why cops get called out on Thanksgiving night." She implored him again, watching his face intently. He leaned back, giving her a measuring look and releasing a long-held breath.

"Tonight it was a shooting; the victims were two sixteen-year-

135

olds," he replied stiffly. His voice was not the mellow, hazy song it could be, but flat and toneless.

"Children!" She couldn't keep the horror from her face. He inched away from her quickly, as though suddenly he were unclean, too soiled to be near her. She groaned, realizing why he was so worried about Nicki and her new friend, crossing her arms over her chest and running warm hands over her arms to stem the bone-chilling draft that gripped her.

She felt total empathy for Captain Antonio DiRocco, but she couldn't really fathom his work, only comfort him. His arms were folded over his chest, a distracted hand stroking his rough beard. She could hear its roughness and the hiss of the fire.

"I'm so cold," she whispered. "Please, hold me." He looked at her with mixed emotions. "Antonio, please." She needed the warmth and security of his arms, and he needed a protected harbor away from his work and the world. He opened his arms without a word and watched her carefully as she turned and curled herself across his lap, snuggling her curves against his hard torso, basking in the warmth of his enveloping embrace. Their bodies fit so well together and felt so right. He held her for a long moment, an eternity, until she could feel her body change from chilled to hot as she soaked up his heat and energy. His hands petted her silken hair and found their way under the tresses to massage her back.

"I need you," he said huskily as she turned her face up to his. He tangled his fingers into the golden torrent cascading over her shoulders and tumbling freely over his arm. His warm mouth pressed against hers, tenderly searching her pink lips with his tongue while alternately nibbling with his teeth, expanding his territory in a journey of discovery. Exploring, seeking, and finding secret, sensitive places on her throat, in the dewy moistness of her mouth, below her earlobe, his touch set her glowing. Her knees drew up toward her chest as passion pulled deep within her abdomen, and one leg stretched in a gracefully seductive motion on the sofa, while the other knee bent, straining the fabric of her robe, pulling it awry, opening the soft wrapper and affording him an enticing view of her lace-framed cleavage. He boldly studied her body, his heated gaze not missing a detail of the translucent perfection of her breasts, so tantalizingly covered. A warm sensation flooded her body at his continued appraisal, and she ached for his touch. Inviting his exploring hands, she pressed her breasts into his muscled chest, gasping softly at the fiery, pleasurable contact.

"God, you make me feel strong," he breathed against her lips as she felt his hardness thrusting urgently into her side. She pulled away from him, alarmed, but he held her tight. "Just ignore it," he said as casually as he could, but his voice was ragged and seductive. "I'm trying my best to."

His mouth took hers in a powerful onslaught, his tongue savagely parting her lips, seeking her sweet surrender. She struggled against him. His mouth softened, lightly caressing her lips, stealing her breath away. He was a gentle knight seducing her chastity, wooing his maiden to his bed with extreme tenderness. He was her dream. He was real.

Her toes curled in splendid anticipation; her arms wound around his neck, hands sliding languidly over the fabric of his shirt as she caressed his back. His hands stole up her side and found the lacy neckline of her gown. A shallow breath caught in her throat when his hand touched her warm, bare skin. He caressed her lips once more, pulling her into a mindless vacuum of pleasure. She knew only that she wanted this man, wanted him to make love to her. She hung on to him and pressed her body closer to him, kissing his mouth, his rough cheek, his neck, breathing in his spicy scent as she nibbled freely on his throat and watched the display of glittering fire streaking across the blackness behind her closed lids.

She melted, quaking into her knight's arms. He was no stranger, but the lover of her dreams. One strong arm cradled her while the other hand glided over the fabric of her gown along her thigh and cupped her bottom as a delicious warm ache contracted again deep within her, causing her knee to draw up and bend close. His knowing hand slid below the robe at her waist, traveled over her ribs, and slowed just below her breast before continuing its journey. With a cherishing touch, he traced over the foamy cloth, his hand moving in slow circles, massaging her breast into a taut peak.

She followed the strong column of his neck with her lips as she lovingly murmured his name, clinging to him, loving him. His

137

breathing was erratic and shallow, but he seemed to be under a tight leash as his hands stopped cruising and playing her body like a maestro with a fine instrument. She implored him with another kiss, but he unwound her arms from around his neck and sat her aside and abruptly moved away from her. He stood facing the fireplace, his body tense like the string of a tightly wrapped bow that still vibrated after the release of an arrow.

She sat frightened and alone on the large piece of furniture, her robe loose and open, the straps of her gown off her shoulders. She ached with desire, body and soul, but her dream had ended. Her legs still stretched out on the couch and she leaned on one hand facing Tony.

"Antonio?" Her voice cracked with longing and fear of rejection. He looked at her, then looked away, muttering an oath under his breath.

He gripped the mantel with both hands. She could see only his stony profile and she noted the muscle flexing along his jaw. *God! He knows,* she thought wildly to herself. *Of course he knows. He can read you like a book. He's had hundreds of women. He knows an inadequate lover when he sees one.*

He was starting to recover his normal breathing rate and she wasn't breathing at all.

"I thought I was tough." He laughed sardonically. "But I can't take this. Not tonight, dragon lady." His tone was deep and low.

He knows. She hurriedly pulled her robe closed and rose silently, backing toward the door. She was mortified. He could feel her beg him to make love to her. She hadn't said it in words, but her body screamed it. He felt that.

"I don't want you, princess. Not this way." She stood frozen in time. Hadn't Kevin always told her no one would want her?

"You don't want me?" she whispered, her voice barely audible. Her vision blurred, she stared down and tightened the belt on her robe. "It's better that way," she croaked, and swirled through the doorway, closing and locking the door behind her.

"Maureen! Maureen, damn it!" She heard his voice and the door rattling, but she had heard it all before. How many times had Kevin told her? But she'd hoped things could be different

138

now with Tony, because she loved him. She had never loved Kevin Ryan. She hoped love would make the difference.

She tripped, panic-stricken, up the stair in the light afforded by the lamp on the drawing table. She was too upset to think about details; she was more concerned about the dull pain in her chest.

She tugged off her robe and looked at the delicate woman in her mirror, remembering Kevin's words when he had come to try to talk her out of their preposterous marriage.

"Mo, I don't know what the hell it is you want from me. I'm not what you need, for God's sake. I don't read the newspaper, except for the sports section. Half the time I don't know what in hell you're talking about!" His tone had fluctuated between pitiable confusion and belligerent anger. More than ever before, Maureen saw the weakness she had ignored because he was her first love. He was pleasant, handsome, a little pompous in his way. She had made him into a man, larger than life, who fought his battles on a football field. But in the end he was merely a boy playing games.

How many times had his words hurt her? had his rough, insensitive lovemaking hurt her?

"You can't want this marriage any more than I do," he had argued. "You really don't think you excite me, do you? You aren't that much of a turn-on, Mo, if you know what I mean. You didn't think there was anything to it, did you?"

Maureen had no answer. Her hands twisted in her lap. Perhaps once they had settled down to a regular life, after the baby was born, she could try to make it up to Kevin, to be more of the woman he wanted. Perhaps . . .

"I'm not ready for a damn wife and a kid," he fairly screamed at her. "I've got to play ball, not house. Don't you see? I might make it into the pros, just like my brothers did. Damn it, Mo!" He turned from her, red-faced and breathing heavily from the intensity of his anger, his large hands balled into fists at his sides. "You might know a virgin would try to put the screws to me. You were just barely there, all uptight and . . . You aren't going to win any prizes in the sack, gorgeous as you are, Mo. I'll tell you that," he ranted bitterly. "What were you saving it for? No one's going to want it anyway."

139

She had sat there and taken it, taken all of it. Vowing to herself that she would survive, she and her child. Though at the time, she had never counted on the scars she would always carry with her.

She sat on the edge of the bed. What was she saving it for? The question brought stinging tears that choked her. She was saving it for her knight in shining armor, wasn't that what Kevin always accused her of? That's who Kevin was supposed to be. Was she wrong about Tony DiRocco too? She was sobbing now.

She knew her marriage to Kevin was a mistake from the beginning and divorce was the only graceful solution. Everyone would be a winner—her parents would be pacified, her baby would have a name, and Maureen could repair her life that her silly dreaming ruined. But before they could agree on a divorce, they each compounded their errors. Maureen became apathetic, and Kevin became hostile and sodden, drinking his cares away, but still blaming her for trapping him. Her participation in the peace rally was just the culmination of many hurts and arguments, and Kevin used it as an excuse to enlist and get out of the marriage.

"You're not the only one willing to take a stand around here, ya know?" He had said that like a hurt little boy. He announced that he was enlisting as he drove her home from the police station.

"Don't you understand." she fumed. "You don't have to go. You don't have to prove anything, Kevin. You have a child."

"So do you. What were you doing out on the streets?"

"Kevin, Vietnam isn't a football game." She breathed deeply.

"Don't try to think for me, Mo," he had shouted. "When I get back I expect this marriage to be over with—ended. Do you understand?"

"If you aren't old enough to raise a family, what makes you think you're grown up enough to fight a war? Kevin, please listen to me. You don't have to do this. We can get a divorce . . . or we can stay together so you'll have deferment after school. . . ."

He lifted his chin defiantly. "It's over, Mo, and I'm goin'."

"I'll get the papers," she had promised. But the paperwork

140

and the bureaucracy of the church moved slowly on ending marriages, especially those with children, much more slowly than Cobra helicopter strikes near the Black Virgin Mountains in Vietnam. Much slower.

The phone rang beside her bed and she gave a startled cry. She answered it quickly so it wouldn't wake Nicki.

"Maureen listen to me—"

She pushed the button and left the phone off the hook. She wouldn't talk to Tony DiRocco again or see him or be wrapped in his arms or hear his voice or . . . She stifled a sob with her hand and lay down in her wide bed. Just a while ago she had imagined lying next to a man she could truly love, a man who loved her. And now she dreaded laying her head down on her pillow. She couldn't close her eyes without conjuring images of Antonio DiRocco. She couldn't sleep, fearing the memories that would invade her dreams. And she couldn't bear any more memories.

She lay staring into the darkness, listening to Tony pace in the room below until he finally settled onto the bed, and the house sank into a crushing silence. It was nearly dawn when she quit tossing on the large bed and fell into a fitful sleep.

CHAPTER NINE

Maureen attempted to work at her drawing table. She couldn't concentrate because that only brought her thoughts back to Tony, and they were too much to handle. She chastised herself for ever letting her hopes and dreams grow. She knew better. She had set herself up for this fall, just like with Kevin. Better now than later, she reasoned, but all the clichés didn't help. She was steeped in misery when Nicki walked into the room.

"Mom?" Maureen looked up, surprised, while her daughter analyzed her. "Are you all right?"

"Sure."

"We're done with the decorating; I think the Christmas lights will look great. Danny helped a lot—he's tall," Nicki said, smiling up at her special friend. The boy hovered above Nicki's shoulders protectively. He was so young and beautiful and Maureen couldn't help but wonder if Tony had once looked that way.

"Yes, of course. Thank you for helping, Danny. I'm glad you could come today."

"I'm happy Nicki asked me." He was quiet and shy, yet his dark eyes hungrily swept her daughter, who made a lovely picture in her soft aqua sweater that contrasted so dramatically with the pink in her cheeks. Nicki would have many young men coming to call; all she needed to do was choose the right one. She was glowing, her timid curves listing toward Danny's lean, sturdy frame wrapped in a brown jacket and blue jeans. The contrast of the two, his dark hair and eyes next to Nicki's pale translucent complexion, happy aqua eyes, and tumbling platinum curls, recited a poem with a contra-rhyme. He put his hand on Nicki's shoulder, reminding her mother that her little girl was growing up. And Maureen wasn't ready, not nearly, for Nicki to leave home in a few short years.

"The day after Thanksgiving the outside decorations go up; it's tradition with us," Nicki said to Danny. The looks they shared were naively potent. "I wished you felt like helping, Mom. Maybe we could go downtown this evening to see the decorations," she said in an obvious effort to cheer up her mother. "Oh, no, I can't. I'm supposed to stay over with Amy tonight," she said apologetically. "Do you mind?"

Maureen shook her head. "That's all right, honey. I'm a little too busy tonight."

"I discovered what was wrong with the phones today," Nicki stated. "The phone in your room was off the hook." Maureen suddenly got an inspiration to draw, avoiding Nicki's questioning glance. "Mom, Danny has to leave now," she said, observing her mother closely.

"Good-bye Danny, and thank you again for helping." Maureen chanced a smile for the boy.

"Yes, ma'am." He stood still and cleared his throat, making no move to leave. "I'd like to see Nicki again if you don't mind, Mrs. Ryan." He held his breath, but there was a determined fierceness in his dark chocolate eyes that told her only Nicki could really send him away.

"I'm not ready for Nicole to be going out on dates yet," Maureen said honestly and firmly. There was a decided silence from the young couple. "But friends that she invites to the house are always welcome." Maureen smiled, wondering where those words came from. Had she planned them long ago? At any rate, they seemed to please and satisfy both of the teenagers, who looked and smiled at each other, then turned to the front door.

Maureen looked down at her work, thinking about how painful young love must be, wondering why she was thirty-four years old with a broken heart, if love was hazardous only for the young. She heard the door open, and a quiet exchange of voices, then the door closed. She felt him before she actually looked up

143

to see Tony standing in the archway, staring at and through her. He was wearing a navy blue pinstriped suit and a white shirt, that seemed even whiter against his dark features. There was a slight bulge under his jacket that covered his tense body, so she knew he'd come directly from work. He should still be at work! She wilted under his belligerently heated gaze, keeping her eyes downcast.

"I don't want to talk to you," Maureen said, swallowing hard. "It'll be better if we don't . . ." She looked up at him, a big mistake, for all her courage drained away. Her arms felt weak, yet he still impaled her with dark, penetrating eyes. "We just don't belong—"

"How could you possibly think I don't want you?" he interrupted. She faded from his directness and anger as he slashed his hand through the air. "How could you possibly think that?" He didn't wait for her reply. He threw both hands into the air, punctuating his list as he spoke. "I've got cases, investigations to run, and all I can think about is you." His arms crashed to his sides as he held her mesmerized gaze. His emotion and sexual vitality were stunning. "I have only a few minutes to talk to you and you take your phone off the hook. Damn it!" She was listening now, not just bracing herself for the passion and energy that broke over her like a wave. "How could you think I don't want you?" He looked down at the hardwood floor. "That's just your new lie, isn't it? You're scared of love, of commitment, that's what it is." He was breathing hard and the veins pulsed at his temples. "But you don't think we should talk about it!" He stepped toward her and she panicked, ready to flee, but he blocked her way. "You're not getting away, Maureen. You're going to listen to me. Damn it!"

"No, Tony . . ." His form blurred through the stinging tears that she willed not to fall but fell anyway. "I know why you don't want me," she said.

"How could you know that?" he shouted, grabbing her arm and pulling her up to her feet. "You don't know," he repeated in a softer tone. "You have no idea how hard it was to pull away from you last night. You don't know. I needed you so badly last night, I could taste it. I needed to make love to you, to fill my life with your sweetness and block out the violence I saw last

144

night. That I see nearly every day. But I didn't want to come to you out of need," he nearly whispered. "Not the first time. Do you understand?"

She shook her head and he exhaled heavily from exasperation. Her eyes closed. She waited. He suddenly released her arm and she stood alone in her own silent limbo of isolation; the only thing she could hear was the pounding of her heart. She stood for a lifetime alone, until his powerful arms embraced her tenderly and she responded to his warmth. She hugged him, letting herself be grateful for his warmth, allowing herself to dream, setting herself up for another fall.

"I didn't want to come to you out of need," he said hoarsely, "because I don't want there to be any doubt in your mind that I love you." He squeezed her to him. "I don't just need you to make love to. I love you. Do you understand?" He hesitated for a moment, then added with intensity, "I want you to love me."

"But last night—"

"I love you and I want to make love to you," he hummed in her ear, pulling her closer still. "I want you to understand that. I want you to know that I don't intend to take you to bed and then forget about you. I love you, see?" She could hear his words, but she was trying to keep a lid on her overflowing heart. He loved her, she loved him, but what about the lesson she had learned from the past?

"Mom?" Nicki's cry from the door startled her. Breaking from Tony's arms and whisking the tears from her eyes, she looked beyond Tony's shoulder to see her radiant daughter.

"Honey?"

"He did it!" Nicki cried, smiling and pleased. "He kissed me!" Tony reeled quickly and started for the door, but Maureen caught his arm, stepping in front of him as though to get a better view of her beaming, blushing daughter instead of calming an irate guardian.

"Are you happy?" Maureen asked, pressing back into Tony, discouraging his touch.

"Wow!" she whispered. "Yes, very. I'm going to go up to my room now." Nicki looked at the older couple, not missing Maureen's smile or Tony's hands resting possessively on her mother's hips. "You both look happy too." She giggled. "I'm going up to my room now," she said broadly. "I have to call Amy. I'll talk to you later," she told her mother quickly before whirling in the center of the room.

"Yes." Maureen smiled. "You'd better call Amy with the news." The teenager breezed from the room and flew up the steps.

Maureen turned to Tony's dark, scowling face and nearly laughed out loud. "For goodness' sake, it was only a kiss. He seems to be a very nice boy. You said so yourself."

"I'm going to talk to Mr. Wonderful," Tony pledged before Maureen could even turn around. "I told him not to get fresh with her—"

"Antonio, the boy was a perfect gentleman all afternoon. He didn't turn into an animal at the front door. Didn't you see her face?"

"I saw." He huffed paternally. "I don't like it. She's only a kid."

"I'm not a kid!" Nicki piped up from the landing.

"Nicole!" Both adults spoke at once, stepping into the dining room to see the young girl still standing at the top of the stair.

"I'll go to my room." She smiled. "You two sound like parents, you know that?" She stood with both hands on her hips, but she was obviously pleased. "Ah, parting is such sweet sorrow," she clowned, leaning over the banister with her hands clasped to her chest as she sighed and then exited stage left to her room. Maureen laughed but envied her daughter's freedom to dream, to hope, to anticipate. She felt Tony's strong arms around her, and she leaned back against his sturdy form, wishing.

"So that's what it means?" He murmured close to her ear, his voice reedy and low.

"What?"

"When a lady gets kissed and she blushes all pretty-pink and her eyes turn a deep, gorgeous blue; it means she's in love."

"Possibly." She smiled, thinking of the child growing into a woman.

"I'm glad," he said in her ear, "because that's the way you look after I kiss you." She stiffened and turned in his arms to face him.

"That's true only for little girls," she hedged, stepping from his arms to avoid his kiss.

"I don't believe you, princess," he said seriously, but a smile crinkled the corners of his eyes. "I've got to go now. Believe me, I don't want to, but I have to get back to work. I'll talk to you later. I need you, want you, love you very much. All I'm asking for is a chance to prove it to you."

"We can't."

"We will."

"No. It will never work."

"Maureen, you don't have to be afraid anymore. I won't hurt you, and I'll make sure nothing else does."

"Who is going to protect you from me?"

"Nothing is going to happen to me. And nothing is going to change the way I feel," he promised. "Nothing."

"You really should go," she said tensely, "while there's still time. Go quickly before I throw myself into your arms and never let you go. Escape before I hold you here."

"I don't have time to argue now." He pulled his watch from his pocket, studied it for a deliberate moment with that habitual motion that seemed to endear him to her all the more. "I'll talk to you later."

"No. There's nothing more to say." She turned her back to him. He swore softly under his breath but didn't press further, slamming the front door with added force as he left the house. *He'll be well and safe,* she prayed under her breath. *He will be.*

It was late and Tony still wasn't home when Maureen stepped into a warm shower. She had told him there was nothing more to say, but she still wanted him home. Was it right to have refused him? She loved him, but what if . . . what if love wasn't enough? It wouldn't work; it would kill her this time. She had to send him away. But what if she never saw him again? She hated all questions and despised all answers, because none of them allowed her to keep Tony.

When Maureen stepped from the shower and turned off the water, she could hear activity in the apartment below. He was home. She dried off quickly, throwing on her robe, tying it, and pulling a brush through her hair. She scampered down the stair. She could hear Tony rushing into the apartment, then slamming

147

closet doors and drawers. She knocked at the doors to his apartment but didn't get a reply except for the raucous noise inside. She released the lock and opened the door, calling his name, but there was no answer. She walked cautiously down the hall toward a softly glowing light in the bedroom, where all the banging and slamming sounds seemed to be coming from.

As she stepped tremulously to the door she saw him throwing shirts and slacks into a soft-sided suitcase flung open on the bed. He was still wearing his navy pinstripe, his jacket off, the vest half open, and the sleeves of his snowy white shirt rolled up. The stark shirt contrasted severely with his earthen tones, darkening his hair and features, making him appear hard and stern. He needed beige not white. He needed a real woman not a pale imitation. She wanted to take his white shirt off and surround him with—if not herself—then warm earth tones, golds and cinnabar, to complement his own rich colors. If she didn't stop him soon, she could color him gone, and she couldn't bear that.

"What are you doing?" she asked redundantly, watching him toss his belongings into the suitcase.

"I can't stay here," he said, freezing like a statue for an instant, then continuing his packing. "I'll get the rest of my things later. But I can't stay here." He evidently planned only to glare and to ignore her, but he looked up at last. His scathing regard scanned her from head to toe, not missing a detail of her appealing figure wrapped in her cranberry satin robe. He searched the low, softly wrapped V-neckline and the enticingly long inverted V at the bottom of the robe for a hint of a gown beneath it.

"Why are you dressed like that?" His voice was tearing fabric.

"I—" The question surprised her; she wasn't thinking about anything but him leaving. "What's the matter with—"

"You look too damn sexy, that's *what*," he said shortly. "I can't stay here!" He grabbed his jacket and slammed the suitcase shut, latching it with undue force and swinging it off the bed.

"Nicki doesn't want you to leave."

He spun on her, instantly outraged. "Don't tell me what Nicki wants! Tell me what you want!" he growled, turning his back on her.

"I don't want you to go," she said barely above a whisper. His

148

stiff, tense back was all she could see, so she couldn't tell what effect her words had on his expression.

"But you don't want me to stay either, do you?" He hated her silence. "Don't worry, you'll find someone else to rent the apartment."

"What upset you so?"

"I just need a new place to live," he snapped coldly, facing her. "It's as simple as that. I shouldn't have moved in here to begin with. It doesn't suit my style." He was breathing fire as he stood defiantly, bag in hand, strong, threatening. "I like smorgasbord, remember?" he sliced at her. "Just get out of the doorway and I'll be out of your house and out of your life, okay?" His penetrating eyes narrowed on her. "And I'll try like hell to get you out of mine." She didn't want him to forget her; the thought of her being banished completely from his memory cut too deep. He must stay. She must make him stay.

"I'm not going to let you go until you tell me what happened." She staunchly blocked his way. She glared at his hard body, sensing the hastily constructed walls he was throwing around himself. As he turned a stony mask toward her, he shut her out.

"So just walk through me, tough guy," she shouted at him, trying to break through the strong barrier and marveling at her own courage. "You're the man of steel; just push me aside," she goaded him as he muttered an oath. Her words were stinging challenges, and she counted on the fact that Tony would never leave a fight. *Fight me, damn it. Don't go! Please.* He abruptly turned his back on her pleading eyes to face the bed.

"Don't turn away!" she shrieked.

"You want to fight?" he asked, wheeling toward her. Retreating from the sheer force of his anger, she faltered to new ground nearer the door.

"You think you can hurt me, dragon lady? C'mon," he sneered, "give it your best shot! C'mon! Do you think you're tough all of a sudden? You're a mosquito-weight, lady; you're not in my class at all," he shouted.

"Then walk right over me, tough guy," she answered, mustering all her courage. *Fight me, damn it. Stay,* her mind reeled. Yet she couldn't think of anything else to say, so she stood riveted in the doorway.

"Is that what you want? Is that how you want to end it?" he said angrily, throwing down the suitcase to the floor, a vein pulsing at his temple. "I'll fight you! C'mon, give it your best shot, hurt me. C'mon. Maybe that's the only way to work you out of my system." He pointed at her menacingly and spoke in a hoarse voice. "But just remember, lady, you've got your shot, then I take mine."

"Tell me what happened."

"What happened!" His hands flew up and he looked at her fiercely. "You happened! That's what!" He began to pace like a caged animal. "I have two homicides, three armed robberies, and an assault to work on, and a lunatic threatens to jump from a rooftop this evening just to make things more interesting. And do you know the only thing I can think about? You!" Animated, alive, beautiful, he gestured hotly with both hands as he spoke. "You!" Both arms crashed to his sides. "All I can remember is how beautiful you are and how much I love you. And how I can't be this close to you and not have you."

"Tony—" she whispered.

"You know what's really crazy? God! What's really insane?" He pounded one balled fist into his open palm with a smack. "I can understand that poor bastard going crazy and deciding he wanted out." He shook his head. "That's the frightening part. He was lonely on the holidays. He just wanted to be with the woman he loved and his kids, that's all, but she turned him away." He looked at Maureen with tortured eyes, narrowing for an instant. "Impossible!" he drawled, staring at her a moment. "Damn it!" He scooped up the suitcase and swung it behind him. "I've got to get out of here!" He tried to get by her, but she forced her way into his path.

"Antonio!"

"I'm going crazy here! I can't have you! I'm jealous of a dead man, for God's sake, because you still love him. Damn it, Maureen! He had his chance. He had you and a beautiful baby. He had it all! But he's gone now. Love me!" he begged her, commanded her. She was shaking her head slowly, not believing anyone could think she was ever in love with Kevin Ryan.

"Tony, I—" she stammered, unable to explain, her bravado depleted.

"You want to fight?" he said hotly. "Let's do it!" He was unrelenting, his eyes searing her until she flushed deeply. He pointed to his rocky jaw. "Right here," he prodded. "Hit me as hard as you can. It'll be better than this pain tearing at my gut, right now. C'mon!" She just stared up at him with wide pools of confusion. "Hit me, damn it! You're afraid to fight me. You're afraid to love me," he baited her, his voice thick with milky venom, his body taut with sexual energy. "Why don't you admit you're a woman with real needs and desires that you can't get from a dead man. You're afraid of a real man!"

In a flash her hand sliced toward his face and contacted with a loud smack on his cheek. He never flinched or looked away from her, and she stared in horror at the angry red welt on his skin, and then at her smarting fingers. She despised herself for hurting the only man she ever loved, especially when he had told only the truth. His muscles flexed ominously along his jaw as he clamped his teeth tightly shut. She started to reach her hand timidly to soothe his cheek when he grabbed it. She heard the door slam behind her, shocking a quailing cry from her as he moved so swiftly she couldn't begin to react. He drove her back, using a hip and thigh for control, and twisted her arm behind her. They both crashed against the closed door, yet he softened the blow with a hand cradling her head and an arm protecting her spine. Her breasts heaving, he trapped her soft body between the door and his long, hard length, yet she was irrationally sure he meant her no harm.

"Now it's my turn, princess," he hissed, tugging gently on her manacled wrist. "And I don't fight fair," he admitted, pulling her arm tighter, arching her lovely bosom up, her robe gaping open to display more cleavage and rounded senuous curves as the fabric of her robe strained over her breasts and slipped from one smooth white shoulder. "Especially when I know what I want and I'm certain I'm right."

"Tony, please . . ." His dark, inquiring eyes disturbed her, so she closed her eyes to keep out his anger, or was it worse—disgust and hate?

"I only wanted to remind you that I could take you whenever I wanted," he said. ":And God knows how much I want you." He eased away from her and released her arm, yet he stayed very

151

close. "But I haven't, and I would never force myself on you." His anger faded, but desire burned from his sweeping gaze as she stood disheveled and stunned. "I'm a man and I love you; I want you to love me. I need to hear you say that you love me." He sucked in air; his features were twisted.

"Antonio." She couldn't face him because he would see the obvious love in her face. Her head dropped forward to rest her forehead on his shoulder, bridling her racing emotions and her rapid breathing. She wanted to tell him she loved him. She wished there was a way to love him without hurting him.

"Can't you pretend? You work with make-believe and dreams every day. Can you make believe you love me, just for a little while?"

"Make believe I love you?" she asked, as if seeing a miracle. Hadn't she been asking herself the same question for days? She could pretend for a while he was hers. Only for a little while.

"Yes," he breathed hopefully. "Can you do that, princess? Can you love me in a make-believe world? God, I love you. Need you."

She nodded, leaning toward his warmth like a plant to the sun. "For a little while," she whispered her agreement as she circled his neck with her arms. A breath caught in his throat as her soft breasts rested willingly against his chest and her hips sought his. She had a make-believe passport to a wild frontier where he would be her guide, and she leaned deliciously into the adventure, embracing him. With any luck at all, she may never wake up from this dream.

"I need you," he vowed, and crushed her to him with a claiming embrace, his hands caressing her soft white shoulders and back covered by the satiny fabric. He pulled her hips to his. His palm smoothed over the curvature of her hips and swirled patterns on the outside of her thigh as his lips took hers in a life-giving kiss, breathing passion into her. His wandering hand slid to the front of her thigh, parting the skirt of the whispering satin and touching the warm velvet of her bare skin. His kiss deepened, but his curiosity rose as his hand journeyed up to her hip, expecting to find lacy panties. He gasped when his hand continued nonstop over warm flesh to where the belt stopped his

152

searing progress. He greedily pulled her hips against his obvious arousal.

"You're very soft," he breathed huskily against her cheek as he loosened the knot in her belt. Soon the cranberry robe hung open and he stood back to look at her body still hidden in the shadows of the fabric. Her blond hair alive with golden light flowed peacefully over her shoulders nearly to her waist, obscuring her large blue eyes as her lips curved ever so slightly into a Mona Lisa smile. He studied her face, gently caressing her delicate mouth, his breathing rapid as he scanned her again. She needed to be unwrapped and enjoyed like a treasured gift, and she would die if he wasn't pleased with what he saw. Her breasts rose and fell erratically with her frantic, anxious thoughts; she was both excited and fearful.

"I don't want to scare you." His eyes swept over her warily. He stood with his hands not quite at his sides, as though he were in suspended animation, and a frown settled between his brows. She was afraid he was going to turn from her.

"I won't hurt you," he promised, assuring her.

She stared at him, disbelieving. This was *her* fantasy too. He would make love to her. In this world she would be a damn good lover, if only once, if only for a little while. Maybe once would be enough. She would draw him to her like a siren on the rocks, lure him, love him. In this dream she was a Venus—an untouchable goddess, a temptress and harlot. But it was impossible to hurt him. Her mouth turned into a timid smile.

He cupped her face with both his strong hands and kissed her lips, tenderly slanting his mouth across hers this way then that, caressing her with utmost care and sweetness. She was trembling from his tenderness. He studied her face and eyes cautiously, then slid both hands down her slender neck, lifting a fall of cascading tresses on his hands and forearms, placing them behind her back, tucking small strands of hair behind her dainty ears. His hands continued their journey over her soft white shoulders, peeling the robe from her body. His regard fell on her high, proud breasts as the satin slipped down her arms and whispered to the floor. He stepped back and she stood rooted, anxiously waiting for his approval or rejection.

She could feel a warm flush start at her cleavage, moving up her throat and down to the very tip of each breast that rose into compact buds under his devouring scrutiny, her bosom thrusting up with each tight shallow breath. His eyes were downcast and partially veiled by long dark lashes, his nearly black hair glistening in the dim light. He was completely dressed, the snowy collar still washing out his golden hues, while she posed naked, glowing and white, like a delicate sculpture of alabaster so easily destructible by one careless move or one rejecting word. If he didn't pull her into his embrace soon, she would scream, but he remained motionless, almost as if the moment were a single frame of film. Her words came out barely above a jagged whisper.

"Don't you want me?"

"Want you?" he croaked, expelling a shaky breath he must have held for hours. "Of course I want you." His eyes lifted and their gazes met so she could see the furnace of desire glowing in the sienna depths. "I want you so much I could . . . You're unbearably beautiful, Maureen. I'm just afraid if I touch you the dream will end."

"Not tonight," she promised, shaking her head slowly.

"No dragons tonight?"

"No dragons," she agreed, and marveled at how well he understood her.

"You're my dream, princess."

"For tonight I'm real," she smiled, stepping to him, draping her inviting arms over his shoulders, and mingling her fingers behind his neck as her sensitive breasts brushed against the harsh texture of his suit, "and I want to make love with you."

She kissed his silent lips lightly and his quaking body overtook hers. He impatiently embraced her with a powerful arm at her back and blocked the natural forward swing of her hips with the other palm, trailing his hand up over her ribs, caressing the concave hollow below her breast, testing its weight with his thumb. He kissed her upturned mouth, filling her with unadulterated pleasure as his seeking hand found the peak of her full, flushed breast, taunting the already excited nipple into a firm, hard tip, celebrating its hardness and her willing compliance, kissing her. His tongue flirted with her quivering lips, and his knowing hand stroked the rosy peak.

She missed the feel of his warm fingers on her back, and she looked up at him, questioning, until she felt a delicate touch, or did she only imagine it? His partially veiled eyes nearly smiled as the caress became more evident, exploring the warm treasures of sensation between her trembling thighs, and she sighed with pleasure. She could hear a fair maiden's song as his hands strummed her body like a mandolin and her mind was set free, floating.

She wanted him badly, as she closed her eyes and pulled his head down to meet her eager lips, as his masterful fingers stroked her, plucking her strings with new vibrant chords, kindling her own flaming passions. Her whole universe was spiraling down to the electric points where her body touched his and he touched her. This was dream and reality wonderfully blended in time, joining past and present in adorned splendor. The familiar consuming sensations contracted the base of her being in a mighty tug, while he caressed, kissed, soothed, and fondled her craving body; she needed him. She prayed she would be good for him, but in this lovely make-believe world, she knew they would be wonderful together.

Pleased with her eagerness and trembling with his own desire, he caught her up in his arms. She pressed her curves into his hard leanness, memorizing his muscled form with her hands. Her strong knight held her in his arms as they soared and floated down together, settling on a soft mattress. She whispered his name over and over, pulling his head down to meet her lips. But he suddenly rose from her and her heart stopped.

"Antonio?" she called, looking at him as he stood by the edge of the bed.

"I don't want to frighten you," he soothed her as he shrugged out of his jacket. "I'll take off my weapon," he explained, tossing the garment on a chair and quickly extricating himself from his holster. He parked the gun and leather on the lampstand near the bed.

"Okay?" he asked as he unbuttoned his vest, dropping it on top of the jacket, the watchchain tinkling, and unfastened the cuffs of his shirt.

"Okay." Her lips turned up. He was apparently so pleased by her expression that his features softened and warmed her with his own winning smile. But it faded as he quickly discarded his

155

shoes and socks and tugged with jerky movements at his tie, freeing himself from it.

"You're a beautiful dream," he said huskily, his gaze caressing her lovely naked body, his features serious and hungry. "I promise I won't hurt you, princess," he said, stepping toward the bed and the regally reclining porcelain figure.

"I know," she smiled, rising and moving to the edge of the bed. She knew he meant her no harm now or ever. She felt sure in this make-believe world that she could be all that he ever wanted.

"Where are you going?" He moved toward her as she knelt on her heels at the edge of the bed.

She didn't answer. She started to undo the buttons of his too white shirt slowly, purposefully, occasionally looking up to meet his ravenous dark eyes. She reached up to slide the shirt from his muscular shoulders and down his powerful arms. Her pale, graceful hands grazed over her golden knight, ruffling over the dark tangle of hair, cruising the scars, finding the gold cross that kept him protected. Her slim, pale form contrasted vividly with his gold tones. She, white and rosy, like the flowers of the open meadow and he, the rich tones of the soil and spice, clay and brown like the earth itself, blended together in perfect natural harmony. She could feel her roots sinking deep, reaching for him, embracing him for her very survival. She kissed his torso, the manly taste and scent delicious as she nibbled and caressed him with her teeth and tongue. He stroked her hair with one hand, seeking and finding her nipple with the other, gasping with pleasure as her fingers unfastened his belt. He suddenly reached over and switched off the light on the stand, plunging the room into a spinning darkness.

"Antonio?"

His breathing was shallow and rapid; his firm, flat abdomen quivered under her caresses.

"Let me love you, princess," he whispered raggedly as he helped her quickly discard his slacks and briefs. "Now."

He lowered her back onto the bed, hovering above her in the darkness, trailing a torrent of hot kisses over her cheeks and down her throat and shoulders. He blazed a sensuous path of passion from her navel over her ribs and breasts, pulling a sensitive nipple into his mouth, teasing with his tongue as his hand

156

found the other peak. She gloried in the freedom to love him with her body and mind as her hands journeyed over the sensual feast of his muscled back, shoulders, and buttocks. His mouth found her tender lips; his tongue entered her mouth with a flurry of passion, he caressing her body with his searing hands, palpating and soothing her passion-starved body as she whispered his name. Gently but thoroughly he guided her over his body to tour that wonderful bold frontier. He paid homage to her lovely form with the praising touch of his hands and lips, not slighting in time or care, as her hands praised and worshiped his fine, strong frame. As he lowered himself onto her, she joyously accepted him, arching her hips up to meet him with a fulfilling sigh. She wanted her knight as much as he wanted his fragile princess, and they joined together. Her lover had been away so long, yet she had saved herself for him and claimed his hard thrusts as he spoke of his love, his waiting, his promise. He had come home to her, and she would have his strength and stamina, cherishing, protecting, loving her—forever. He was home. They were mated in a wonderful dream of ecstasy. Spinning, arching, she clung to Tony, pulling him deeper into her vibrating center, drawing him to her at last as she wrapped all her bare, smooth velvet limbs around him. They imploded into an internal fire of passion that consumed them both in eternal love.

They were one.

She was loved and desired.

Trembling, they clung to each other, caressing, loving, stroking, completing each other in the most human way, fulfilling the other's desires, pleasures, dreams. She ecstatically drew in the vital essence that he gave so freely. Clinging together until subsiding in an enjoyable stillness and caring, he rested upon her and she savored his warmth and love. She knew immediately, basking in the afterglow, that making love with this man once was not enough. Once was a torture she couldn't endure, so she allowed herself to dream of a lifetime together. She kissed his cheek and nibbled on his neck, savoring the taste and feel of him.

He lay beside her and gathered her to him with a pleased sigh, kissing her forehead and fingering strands of long silk hair. They fondled and kissed, whispering loving words to each other over and over. Allowing their excitement to mellow into serene contentment, warming each other as Tony pulled a blanket over them, they rested for long, gratifying moments. Neither spoke for a long time, both unwilling for the dream to end.

"What do you think, princess?" he asked at last as he tucked the blanket around them.

"I think it was magic," she purred, snuggling to him, gracefully stretching one arm and draping it over his chest.

"That good?"

"Yes," she whispered, sliding a bent knee over his thighs to inch closer to him. Then she panicked. "What do you think?" Maureen asked, holding her breath with evident uncertainty, looking up at him in the darkness.

"Wow!" he breathed, imitating Nicki. "You're terrific!" He gave her a hug.

"Don't tease me, Tony, not about this."

"I'm not," he said seriously, tracing the delicate curve of her mouth with a finger. "I was right all along; we're great together."

"You're very sweet," she whispered, kissing his palm.

"Sweet? Hey, I've got a tough reputation to uphold, lady!"

"Ummm-hmmm . . ." she crooned devilishly.

"What do you mean by that?" he asked roughly as gentle, inquiring fingers rounded over her hip. "What does 'ummm' mean?"

"It means I want to . . . hmmm . . . you know."

"No, tell me." She could imagine his grin by the sound of his voice. "You want to make me a very happy man, right?"

"Yes."

His mouth discovered her parted lips for a soft caress. "Then tell me about you and me—together," he said. "You know I love you."

"Tony . . ." Her pliant body tensed in his arms. "Let's not talk about that now. Let's enjoy the magic in our make-believe world, please."

"I'm sorry, princess, I need more."

"I don't want to argue with you."

"Why not? You were ready to fight before."

"We're making love not war, Captain." She grinned.

"And it's great," he assured her, bussing her hairline. "But—"

"But I don't want to talk about it. Because you could argue with the devil himself and win."

"Oh! You're afraid you'll lose this fight?"

"I . . . I . . ."

"Maybe if you lose this one, we'll both win."

"Antonio, please."

"I can't help it," he said, bracing himself up on an elbow. "Maybe it's the lawyer in me instead of the crusty, tough cop."

"Police officer," she corrected him, then expanded deliciously. "Captain Antonio DiRocco, Twenty-Eighth Street Station—"

"I want you to be my wife," he interjected. "I need your sweetness and beauty to keep me from getting old. This is an ancient man here. I need you to—"

"You don't feel so old to me, Captain," she murmured, skimming her hand over his chest, finding his cross dangling on its chain temptingly near his flat nipple. "You feel fantastic to me," she said as her pleasing fingers traveled generously over his chest. "I love to touch you," she said seductively as her fingertips explored him with butterfly lightness and a breath caught in his throat. "I love to kiss you." Her tender mouth found his, seeking her caress, meeting her tongue. She loved making love with him, and her body ached for him again. "I love to . . . ummm . . . listen to your voice."

He rolled her onto her back with a playful shove, laughing. "You love my voice?" he queried as he hovered above her, framing her face in his hands.

"Uh-huh!" she answered saucily, her hands resting lightly on his shoulders, waiting with delighted anticipation.

"That's too bad, doll, 'cause I'm through talkin' with ya," he drawled before his mouth covered hers.

"I was hoping you'd say that," she whispered happily, pulling him down closer to her as his kiss deepened.

They didn't speak again with words but with acts of patient love and sweet, tender passion, affording complete pleasure at a tantalizingly lazy pace. Loving, giving, sharing, the princess and the knight made love again in their beautiful blooming meadow before they drifted off together into a deep, restful sleep, saving their dreams for their waking.

CHAPTER TEN

Maureen awoke with Tony's arms wrapped around her. Stretching languidly, she basked in his strength and warmth as she listened to his steady breathing. She studied the sleeping sounds of the man she loved, thinking she needed to know all about him, know this battle-weary knight. In the still of the night it not only seemed possible for them to be lovers, but it was very good and right. She resisted measuring anything mundane like time in her wonderland of innocent love, but she guessed their fragile dream wouldn't survive the light of dawn. Pressing her bottom back against his thighs, marveling at how well their bodies fit together, she vowed to enjoy the remainder of her fantasy. He pulled her closer to him as he awakened slowly.

"Princess?" He spoke in a sleep-worn whisper. She rolled away from him, putting a little distance between their cozy bodies as he turned onto his back and put one bent arm under his head, while the other arm cradled hers. His abdomen shuddered its response as her hand grazed its length, finding the long, scarred welt on his trunk.

"How did you get this?" Maureen asked, stroking the scar.

"I told you," he retorted, feigning sleepiness or disinterest as his hand rubbed over his beard.

"What happened?"

"Hey, you didn't want to talk, remember?"

"Did you catch the men who did it?"

"Yeah."

"What happened?" He breathed out heavily and put a sure hand on the inner curve above her hip.

"Four out of the six got assault with intent. One got life for aggravated murder—"

"Murder? Who got killed?"

"I'm in heaven, touching someone soft and beautiful, and you want to talk about things like that?"

"Tell me. I'm not a child, Tony."

"I know," his rough voice inflected as his hand slid up, his thumb brushing the side of her breast. "But in some ways you're so innocent. . . ." Her arm clamped down on his hand with what she hoped was squelching toughness.

"Who was killed?"

"You'd make a great interrogator, you know that?" he teased her. "But these entrapping methods of making a man talk would be frowned upon by the department." He wriggled his hand, finding his sensuous target. "But I have no complaints."

"Tony, tell me, please."

"It happened a long time ago," he said grimly, lifting his hand from her. He was silent a moment, remembering, forgetting. She watched him in the darkness but couldn't distinguish his expression; he was scarcely breathing at all.

"Who was killed? Was it your partner?"

"Yeah," he sighed. She snuggled into him, attentive, understanding. "Jack Cluny was an old Irish cop. A giant! As big as a house, he was," he intoned with his impression of an Irish brogue. "With a heart to match," he added in his own voice, "but he kept that fact well hidden. You have to on the job," he reflected honestly, pausing to remember, then chuckled low near her ear. "The Hardy Boys we weren't. He was old, or at least he seemed that way to me as a rookie. But he never wanted to be anything but a beat cop." He fell silent a moment. "Anyway, we walked right into an ambush one night. It was supposed to be an officer-in-trouble call and it didn't take long to discover that we were the ones in trouble. Old, tough Cluny and the rookie." He chuckled. " 'Be tough, kid, be smart, you'll be a good cop,' that's what he told me every day."

161

"You are good," she said, her free hand resting lightly on his chest, toying with his crisp, tangled hair. "You care, Antonio."

"I love you, do you know that?" His hand glided along her arm and down her ribs, her body purring in response. "You're so sweet . . . you don't need to hear any more."

"Yes, I do." Anything that was important to him was important to her. And she knew by his tenseness that the incident was an old, festering wound, not the neat surgical scar on his beautiful torso. She trailed her hand down to find the white track. "What happened?"

"There were six of them, part of a gang." He spoke as though he were merely telling a story that happened to someone else; the walls he built were slowly crumbling. Someday, she hoped, they would come down completely. "They got the jump on us. It was a stand-off. Two held Jack, each with a knife at his throat, and I held a gun on one of them. It was a stand-off. I could get one, but the other . . . If I didn't put my gun down, they were going to kill him. Cluny told me to shoot, that he was a dead man anyway. But I had to try. As soon as my gun hit the ground the other four jumped me and Jack hit the ground shortly after. They told me I wasn't worth a bullet, not a cop, they'd just beat me to death like a dog. They nearly did." She shuddered, holding him at the thought of such cruel hatred directed toward the man she loved. "All the rookie could do was watch Cluny die. If he would've shot like he was told, maybe . . . maybe . . ."

"He wanted you protected. That was the only reason he told you to shoot, to help even the odds for your escape," she said earnestly. She was beginning to understand more about Antonio DiRocco, the lover-friend. Maureen moved closer to him, giving his cheek a gracious kiss, settling her head on his shoulder, her breasts gently nudging his side. His arms circled her again, pulling her closer still as he kissed her hair. "If it happened again, what would you do?"

"I've spent years becoming so tough and so smart, it wouldn't dare happen again."

"But what if . . ."

"I don't know." She could tell by his tone that he had replayed it over and over, in thoughts and nightmares, but the results were clouded.

"I do," she stated firmly. "You'd put down your weapon; you'd try to save the victim." She recalled the first day she had met him, when he spoke of seeing too many victims young and old. Didn't he tell her that's why he decided to be a cop? Her hand traveled over his chest and she pulled herself nearer to his long length as his hands stroked her back.

"What makes you so sure?"

"You are the brave knight," she whispered half-joking, trying to lighten the mood that had become so serious.

"The knight?" His tone mellowed to an infectious blues song. "Am I the true love of the Princess Maureen?"

"You . . . you and I are just make believe."

"No, no. I don't buy that." His voice was a low croon. "Making love once might be pretending. Twice is something else."

"What about three times?"

"Three times?" She could barely see his white teeth in the smile she heard.

"Three times is magic."

"No magic, princess," he chuckled, "until you tell me you really do love me."

"No magic?" she challenged him. "You don't want to make love?"

"Not until you admit you love me."

"We will," she said impishly, propping herself up on an elbow, looking down at him, trying to discern his expression in the darkness. She could see he wasn't smiling.

"You wanted to talk before; now I want to talk about us," he said earnestly. "I want you to marry me."

"Could we negotiate that later and concentrate on other things now," she said playfully, gently straightening strands of the dark hair on his chest.

"No, we can't."

"But you forget, Captain, you're in my make-believe world now. I have magic too," she said. "So we will make love."

"We won't," he said firmly, and then teased her. "That's all you can think about! Don't you know that's when all the—ah—complications begin? I want you to be my wife; it's as simple and as complicated as that."

"We'll make love now and talk later." She nibbled on the warm column of his throat.

"We won't!" Her hand flowed over his flat abdomen and over his chest. "We won't," he repeated, but a telltale breath caught in his throat.

"I have magic, Captain," she promised in a whisper as her hand trailed over the crisp hair of his chest and down over a smooth, jutting hipbone.

"Maureen," he whispered huskily, "tell me you love me." She would rather show him; she needed to show him.

"Magic." That was the only word she could push through her constricted throat. She lowered her head and nibbled on his chest as her hand glided up on the inside of his thigh. Her tongue flicked over her hardened nipples and his breath was labored with battle and desire. Her lips met his eager mouth and their tongues intertwined in a moment of sweetness as her hair cascaded down, forming a fragrant golden curtain around them, blocking out the outside world. He became her universe as his hands moved over her entreating form. He played her body like the minstrel strumming a heartfelt melody, as his knowing hands thrilled and excited her.

The song was low and familiar, always the same, about the bold knight who rescues his princess, setting her free, body and spirit, through love and daring. She joyously responded to the troubadour's new poem. His abdomen quaked as her hand wandered across his flat plateau, as she rose to settle lower. His fingers cruised and soothed over her breasts, finding the scented valley between them, creating new stanzas of heroic verse and she answered with her own medieval rhymes, singing along with her beautiful, sensuous serenader. She kissed his belly, snaking her tongue to meet hot flesh, alternately kissing and nibbling over the quivering muscle, bathing his body in her love, returning to him the splendor that he gave her. He praised her body with tender, loving poems as knowing fingers sensitized her taut rosy peaks, as her hand encircled his maleness like a gently tendril of a vine clinging to a rock, while Tony groaned his pleasure.

"I'll always love you," he pledged as he pulled her up onto him. He vowed his love in a husky song, low and sensual, spoken

164

in a moist, reedy tone. She parted her legs, welcoming him onto her pliant, giving shore in a rolling tide of passion. He pulled her mouth down to meet his in an unmistakable claim of their destiny. Accepting, answering, she kissed him, nibbling his full lower lip, flirting with her ravenous mouth. "You make me strong." His words thrilled her, for she was part of her knight's strength and courage. She enjoyed his heat and his forceful thrusting, but she couldn't have enough of his strong body.

She folded her legs back and pushed up on her hands, arching her spine as he thrust up and up, while his seeking hands found her proud bosom, begging for his caress. Their hands and bodies moved in a lyrical cadence, conceiving new rhymes, reciting the tales of chivalrous deeds, exchanging praises to the brave knight and the fair maiden in odes of love. Her fingers spoke in classic iambs as she touched his neck and torso, ran over the length of his flexed biceps and banded forearms. She loved his body so—lean, strong, part of her. He lifted his head and pulled an excited rosy peak into his mouth, teasing with his tongue until she repeated his name in a whisper that was far away, of another land, another time. To man, to woman, to love's abounding might. Love conquers all, love wins always. An intense sensation drew him deeper and deeper into her very core, finally exploding within her.

"Antonio," she moaned as he pulled her down to him, surrounding her with his arms as they shuddered together, reciting a new poetry, a new song in their medieval world. *I love you*, she shouted. Her words were so far, far away, in another time. He gave her energy with his pulsing vitality, and she was filled, loved, loving. Their hearts beat together, blending into a rapturous choir. There was only their mystical world where two souls were one, their ecstatic bodies moving in ancient rhythms, in legendary odes. She knew in her heart he would always return to her and she would forever love her knight. Always. She soaked in his energy, his love, his vital essence, as his hands lovingly massaged the base of her spine. The movements subsided inside her and she rested spent but content upon him, while she nestled her cheek against his shoulder and he stroked her hair.

"Did I hurt you?"

"I'm fine," she sighed, and nibbled his neck as a final small but pleasant surge warmed her center. He moaned and embraced her, lifting her head to meet his warm lips.

"Was it magic?" she asked with a smile. She suddenly realized she could see him. It was getting light.

"Yes," he said, slanting his warm open mouth across hers, kneading her soft white shoulder with a loving hand. The wanton mistress subsided and cuddled demurely atop him, sweet, innocent, rutilant with a dewy camelia hue. Knowing she had brought him to waves of passion, she was content. If nothing else in her magic world of make believe, she had loved him not once, not twice, but three times. Could that last her a lifetime? She knew the lonely answer. She was so saddened by the dawn, the dull gray light turning a hazy blue as the mystical hours waned.

"It's getting light," she said sadly. She started to move from him.

"Don't go."

"I have to."

"No," he said fiercely.

"Antonio, this was just pretend."

"No." He held her closer. "And it wasn't all magic either. It was you and me in love. It was wonderful because we love each other." He squeezed her to emphasize his words.

"It can't be."

"Why not?"

"We just aren't right for each other." She fumbled about, moving beside him.

"How can you say that?" He looked at her, studying her face for a truer meaning. "There's been wild chemistry between us from the first moment we met. That's why we've fought each other so hard. That's why we . . . we just made love with each other . . ."

"For one night," she finished his sentence. She was shaking her head. "We're opposites."

"Haven't you ever heard the old theory that opposites attract?"

"Tony. Let's be sensible."

"No way, lady. It's too late for that." He smiled at her.

"I was foolish once before. I fell in love with a man who was completely different from me. We didn't think or feel the same,

166

or didn't even like the same movies or the same thing to eat for breakfast. It didn't work!"

"How about bacon and eggs?" he teased her.

"Tony!"

"I appreciate your differences very much," he said as a hand glided over her sensuous mounds, finding a cozy resting-place for his palm. "I like the idea that you know when not to be a lady, milady," he teased her.

"Tony, please."

"We just made love to each other. Don't tell me you're getting shy again." He ruffled her ear with his finger. "I love that too."

"Tony," she said, curbing the heat rising to her cheeks.

"I love you—your idealistic dreaming, your innocent goodness. I need you to hold the big bad world at bay, princess."

"But a man like you . . . hmmm . . . needs . . ." She faltered, flushing deeply.

"Tell me, what do I need?" He chuckled. "You spent the entire night in my arms and you can't tell me what I need."

"No," she whispered.

"You haven't been listening. I need you."

"That can't be."

"Why not? Bodies don't lie; they don't pretend. And your soft, tender body was loving mine, begging for me to love you. You can't deny it."

"I . . . I . . ."

"For the first time in my life I made love with a woman I love," he confided, brushing a thumb over a responsive nipple. "And it was perfect. Not make believe, not magic, but love. That's what I need for a lifetime."

"No," she whispered.

"I need a shy, caring wife that sets me afire, makes me glad I'm alive. I need you to take care of, so I'll be strong and complete."

"Tony, please." She struggled away from his engulfing intensity.

"Maureen, don't go!" He held her and she relaxed beside him, too weak to resist his plea. "Please, I know I come on too strong for you." He breathed out his frustration. She wanted to stay by his side always, to relish his strength, to bask in his heated desire.

Knowing that she had the power to bring him to such a feverish pitch of excitement was a glorious, heady feeling.

"Will you marry me?" Would his love suddenly dissolve one day, when the novelty of such an unlikely match had worn thin, the way it had so many years ago? She looked so deeply into his eyes that she could almost, but not quite, decipher the future. She couldn't take the risk, not of crippling her bold, brave knight.

"I don't want to hurt you." She shook her head.

"Then say you'll marry me."

"No." Her voice cracked. "I told you, making love only makes things more complicated."

"Making love with someone you love makes it beautiful, and you know it," he insisted. He stopped short, breathing hard. "We're good for each other, damn it. Stop fighting me and make me a very happily married man!" He wrapped her stubborn beauty in his arms again. "I'll love and cherish you."

"No!" The word stunned him so, that the strong bands released her and she slid from his arms and rose from the bed. Once in motion, she continued to scoop up her robe and to shield her delicate beauty from him.

"I want and need you, Maureen. What more can I say?"

"Promise me you'll be safe and unharmed." She was near tears. "Promise me what we feel will last forever," she challenged him.

"There are no guarantees. But I'm off the streets now."

"That's the lesson I learned from Kevin Ryan. No happily ever after. God!" She choked on her fear. "I couldn't bear it if anything happened to you . . . if we someday ended up hating each other, just the way . . ." His incredulous stare caused her to stop mid-sentence. "Don't you see I'm afraid to love you?" she asked quietly.

"Nothing will change the way I feel."

"You don't know that!" She stood half recalling, half foreseeing, still clutching the cool satin to her bosom. "What if one day, not right away, but one day you felt trapped or cheated?"

"Trapped? What do you mean, trapped?" He was trying to follow her thoughts, but his decoder was jammed with too many messages, all conflicting, like the desire and fear bouncing in her

168

brain. "I want you. You're the only woman I've ever wanted to marry—ever."

"I'm afraid!" she screamed as she disintegrated into quaking fear. He watched her for a long moment, then looked away. He sat up, bracing his back against the headboard of the bed and the sheet slipped down his torso to settle seductively low over his hips. He started to speak, but halted. He searched her eyes for answers. She gazed at the body of the man she loved, strong, scarred, suddenly untouchable.

"You know what's really ironic?" His voice was rough and familiar, and he did not wait for her reply. "I was afraid of loving you at first because I didn't want to run the risk of getting hurt again. People I get attached to tend to leave me somehow. . . . I thought if I could talk myself out of loving you, I wouldn't have to take the risk of feeling as if my heart had been torn out by the roots—the feeling I've got right now. I was afraid of losing you." He watched Maureen wrapping herself in her robe and her will of iron. "Hell, I can't lose something I never really had. Can I?"

"No." He flinched as she said the word softly. He stood firm, but died inside. She walked slowly to the door.

"Maureen." She turned to look at her golden-skinned crusader—piercing eyes, rocky jaw, sleek, hard body.

"Thank you for"—she drew a shaky breath—"for last night. I—"

She turned quickly and started up the hallway. "The only way you can really hurt me is not to love me." He called out to her. She walked stiffly toward the large double doors while she had the courage and the will to walk away from him. She would walk away before she drove him away.

"One night isn't enough!" he shouted at her. "You're killing me by walking away." She stopped in her tracks. "Maureen!" Silence followed and her heart broke as the stillness thundered in her ears along with her pounding heart. She heard her life's blood swishing in a torrent through her temples, but there was no movement in her legs. She stood planted in the large archway, unable to proceed or go back. She was a dreamer, still trying to cling to sleep, struggling to go back to a fantasy that the morning

169

light and consciousness had burned away. She was afraid to take the chance that her dream could ever come true.

The bleak, hazy darkness was ahead, his warmth and light behind. She needed him. She would be the waste of a wilted flower missing Tony's deep fertile earth to root and thrive in. She needed his stamina, vitality, and strength. But he didn't call her name. She wavered in the wide-open doorway, the house creaking and no longer divided by the doors, but she was splintered into shards of pain.

"If you walk through that door, you'll kill the brave knight, and I know you can't do that."

"Antonio." She was so comforted to hear his voice again. She turned to look at him, framed by the morning light arcing through the beauty of the stained glass window.

He was tense, but his voice was confident. Could she risk loving him? "Don't shut the door on our love, Maureen." She cherished his body with her eyes. His lean torso was bare; she looked at that same marvelous body she had worshiped with her hands and caresses only moments before. He had pulled on slacks that rode low on his hips and nearly covered his bare feet. His hands were jammed into his pockets. She couldn't take her eyes off him. When she thought she'd seen enough, another interesting feature would catch her eye and her imagination. His eyes seemed dark and mournful. She wished . . .

"It wasn't me that made you afraid to love. I'd never hurt you. You know that?" he said.

"Yes." He was noticeably relieved by her quick, unconditional answer. His shoulders relaxed.

"But we might hurt each other." Her voice was pleading. "Don't you understand why I'm afraid?" His gaze was unwavering, confused. "I thought I was in love with Kevin Ryan, and by the time we both woke up I was carrying his child and Kevin didn't want anything to do with me or the baby. We married and lived like strangers and before it was over we nearly ended up destroying each other." She couldn't deny that she loved Tony. "I'm just afraid to trust my feelings."

"That won't happen again with us, Maureen." His eyes were tortured. "It's not the same with you and me, damn it! I love you. I told you that. If you can't trust what you feel, trust what *I* feel."

170

"I—I'm afraid I'll disappoint you, drive you away. I couldn't stand that," she finished with a whisper.

"Hey, I'm not going anywhere."

"Not yet."

"Damn it! How old were you when you knew Kevin? Eighteen, nineteen? You were a kid, and so was Ryan," he insisted. "Neither of you knew what you wanted or felt. It wasn't your fault he went to 'Nam or got injured. It happened. You were kids." He lifted her chin with his fingers and peered into frightened, misty eyes.

"Tony, please . . ." She closed her eyes tightly.

"Believe me, I'm no kid. I know exactly what I want." Her troubled blue gaze engulfed him, and her lips parted. "I know what you want too." It had to be written all over her being, in every breath she took and every beat of her heart.

"No, you don't," she blurted out. "You can't, because I don't know," she lied boldly. She withdrew from him, realizing she disappointed him badly. "See? I'm hurting you already."

Tony muttered an oath and stepped toward her, but she darted away from his outstretched hand. He cursed again, apparently hating her retreat.

"I always go after the truth, you know that. It's an occupational hazard." His voice had a hard edge to it.

"No, you're never afraid of the truth, Tony, but I am." She couldn't look him in the eye. "The truth is too . . . too—I'd rather have make believe." She swallowed hard.

"We can make it work."

"No, we can't." She looked at him, stunned, and then ran across the dining room and up the stair.

"Maureen, listen!"

She stopped on the stair and looked back down at him from a higher, safer distance.

"I couldn't bear it if you discovered that you hated me someday." Maureen was trembling now, clutching to her strength. "So let's end it now before we really hurt each other." She ran up the steps and stood near the landing. Tony went toward the her, but she only retreated farther, so he stopped.

"It's too late for that!" He rubbed a distracted hand over his rough beard and raked fingers through his dark hair. "You're in

171

my blood, Maureen Ryan, and I don't see any cure." His quiet words seemed to come straight from his heart and she hated her own self-doubt, especially in contrast to Tony's strength.

When she looked down, Tony had already begun to pull the doors shut. She was too frightened to love him, but petrified of losing him. "Tony, please." The doors continued to close. "Tony, don't go," she said in a small voice.

"I've got to. I can't be near you and not have you, princess. I'm sorry, I'm just not tough enough for that." She sucked in a panicked breath. "When you realize that you aren't dreaming and want to tell me that you love me, when you can tell me the truth, then come and talk to me." His voice was firm, but his eyes suffered. "I came to rescue you, princess, but you wouldn't let me carry you off into the sunset. I'm going to leave the key with you, so you can come to me. When you're ready, come and talk to me."

"Where are you going?" She was a lost, trembling child.

"You'll be able to contact me at work."

"Tony, please."

"Good-bye, Maureen," he said as the doors rolled shut with a solid knock. When she heard the lock, her heart stopped. The cold sound of metal striking metal as the lock tumbled into place sent a cold chill down her spine that swept over her body and wobbly limbs. Minutes later she heard him walk out the back door and drive away, and the bottom dropped out from under her, plunging her into an infinite icy abyss.

He wanted the truth. But what was it? The only truth she recognized now was that all her dreams and hopes had just walked out the door and she sat alone. She was certain only that she would be miserable without him, without his love. What was true? What was a dream?

Tony was gone.

Watching the door and the oak spindles of the open stairway, she huddled and rocked on the steps, her arms hugging her knees.

CHAPTER ELEVEN

Maureen hibernated. At work she busied herself as a background artist, painting safe blue rivers and peaceful green forests, avoiding meadows of wildflowers and her knight's dark eyes, Tony's eyes, beseeching her to go to him, tell him the truth. Vaguely the monstrous, fire-breathing dragon haunted her, demanding her study. Where did he come from? Who sent him? The creature sprung full-blown from her mind, and then she copied it repeatedly, sketch after sketch, until it came alive. Just as she had confessed her failure with Kevin over and over, day after day, year after year, until it was real. Her brain feigned indifference to the litany of messages of self-destruction, but her survivor's heart knew.

How many times in the last week had she picked up the phone to call Tony, aching for the sound of his familiar low-timbred voice. But her fear held her in check, causing her to retreat back into her work and her quiet pain.

She numbed her brain, because thinking of him, remembering, brought only heartache. Maureen was no stranger to this dark, dismal place. Many years ago, after Kevin's death, and long before she'd put her life back together, she had lived in this shadowland. Her daughter still needed her, and the film required her sketches, so she fought to gather herself into one effective, efficient piece. The lonely survivor would spin a steely silk thread of her tenacious will and pull her own weight along, inching her

173

way back to life in a world devoid of dreaming, a world without Tony. Her freed spirit had soared and dreamed, because her knight awakened the princess from a dreamless sleep with a kiss. But now her life would be back to black and white no more Technicolor, wide screen, and CinemaScope. So she retreated into herself a while longer, not yet able to face the mundane bleakness before she started her long, tedious journey back.

Only news that Tony was in danger had the power to bring her back to life again. Alive with a desperate sense of dread and urgency. Tony was in danger! She didn't understand how he could be threatened. A mid-morning robbery attempt on the Near South Side had first developed into a shootout with police and then stabilized into a stand-off.

Hoping to bargain for a lesser charge, the armed thief had scrambled back into the store and claimed six shoppers and a store manager as hostages. William Brown was described on the news as a man allegedly dangerous, with many previous arrests. Amid the static voices of radios and TV, each tuned into a different station, Maureen paced from room to room, her heart jumping into her throat at each new bit of information. Nicki tried to comfort her with gentle and patient words, more as a friend than as a daughter. But there was little consolation for Maureen as she prowled before her drawing table. For hours she'd been unable to function, only praying she would get the chance to tell Tony that she loved him.

It was no real surprise when she heard the report that Police Captain Antonio DiRocco of the Twenty-Eighth Street Station had gone into the store unarmed, to negotiate the release of the hostages. When she heard that the first five hostages were released, she was happy for the freed people but frightened for Tony. She knew Tony would try to rescue the hostages no matter what, to lay his nightmares about Cluny and his own doubts to rest.

She trekked miles in the confines of the sitting room, her mind filled with questions and memories of their beautiful night together which was never far from the rippling surface of her thoughts. For peaceful moments a clear pool in her mind's eye reflected like a perfect mirror, where she could see their love-entwined bodies, sensual and sublime in that dreamworld. He had said he loved her, had cherished her with his touch, and had sworn that she was a vital part of him. She loved him and needed his strength, his truth. If only she could be braver like her knight who rode tall and undaunted.

When the doorbell rang she surged with irrational hope, thinking it could be Tony, anticipating his kiss and embrace. Maureen rushed to swing the door wide to find Myron Feldman on her front step.

"Myron," she said, choking back tears.

"Damn that maniac," he said, embracing her. "He breaks your heart by not coming back for seven days and then he does something crazy like this!" he shouted, guiding her back into the sitting room.

"It's all my fault," she said.

"How can it be your fault?" She stared at Myron, hearing the echo of Tony's words. She could still see Tony's frown of disbelief when he realized she blamed herself for Kevin's injuries. He begged and commanded her to see that it wasn't her fault. Her mind knew why Tony voluntarily became a hostage. He had to. She wasn't responsible for his decision any more than she was for the choice of a boy that went to war.

"Why did he do a crazy thing like this?"

"It's an occupational hazard," she said, attempting a laugh that only ended in a bitter croak.

"Any fool could see you were in love with him. Why didn't he know that?" Myron growled.

"He did. I was the fool! I refused to admit it. Oh, Myron," she groaned, leaning her head on his shoulder. "I may never see him again." Tears held in check for several hours rolled freely, and her shaky knees collapsed as she plunked listlessly down onto the couch. "I was so afraid if I married Tony that it wouldn't work out, or that something horrible would happen to him. You know, like it did to Kevin. God, I couldn't bear that! And now he's . . . he's threatened." Her mind refused to estimate the vicious possibilities. "I'm afraid I won't have the chance to tell him that I love him."

"Why did he volunteer himself?"

"He had to," Maureen said deceptively calmly, tapping a

reserve of strength to dry the tears and collect her wits. "There were innocent people in the store during the robbery."

"But the police have negotiators, SWAT teams, and what have you!"

"There were seven people in that store; now there are only two young girls and one tough cop being held." She understood what he was doing. It was the culmination of a chain reaction triggered long ago by an officer-in-trouble call. It was a code, a promise, a noble cause, just between him and Cluny. It had nothing to do with her, but with who he was and who he needed to be. Maureen knew she loved Tony. He was her faithful knight who lived a creed of another age, and she hoped it wouldn't get him killed in this frightful era of no honor.

"For heaven's sake, there's no such thing as a hero in this day and age!" Myron cried, walking away in exasperation. "Doesn't he know that!"

"You . . . you can tell Tony that," she stammered. "I just want to tell him I love him."

"Mom, you'll have a chance to tell him." Nicki sat down beside her. "I know you will. You don't need to be afraid anymore. Nothing's going to happen to him. Nothing."

"Tony told me the same thing," she said, hugging and kissing her daughter.

"See. Tony wouldn't lie," Nicki assured Maureen.

"No. He's very big on truth," Maureen agreed, giving her daughter an extra hug. "I love you very much, do you know that?"

"I know," Nicki said quietly, then added, "How could the princess and knight not live happily ever after?" Mother and daughter clung to each other, rocking gently. Yes, how could she have cheated herself out of a loving life. All she needed to do was tell him what was in her heart all along. Did she drive him away even before they had had a chance to be a family? No. She would tell him; they would love each other.

"Maureen!" Myron called. "It was just on the radio, the last two hostages are supposed to be released soon."

"He'll be in there alone?" Maureen choked, panic gripping her. "I've got to go! I've got to see him, talk to him."

176

"You can't! The police have the whole area blocked off," Myron reasoned. "They'd never let you in. It's too dangerous!"

"I've got to go!" Maureen insisted, rushing to grab her coat and her keys. She would tell him the truth, promise her love. Maureen couldn't keep him on paper or film or locked in her mind as a memory of a dream. She had to set them both free, to take a chance and let the dream awaken and live.

"Maureen!"

"Please, Myron, stay with Nicki!"

He nodded. "I'll take her home with me, don't worry. But call us!"

"I will," she tossed over her shoulder as she headed for the door.

"Just bring that grouchy old cop back home where he belongs, and remember to tell him I love him too," Nicki said.

"I won't forget." She walked back to meet her daughter for a quick embrace before scrambling out the door. He would be safe and she'd tell him that she loved him, she vowed as she willed herself to drive at a decent speed across town to the South Side of Chicago.

Maureen realized they were opposites, but, like bookends, they completed each other. Together they were idealistic, strong, romantic, cynical, and brave, but apart they were only halves. Half of love is no love at all. And she wanted it all. She wasn't afraid anymore. There wasn't a dragon to keep them apart, because the dragon was dead, slayed by the love of one man. Free of her fear and guilt, she could be dreaming or awake, but she would always love him forever. When he saw her he would catch her up in his strong arms, capturing her in a loving caress. They'd be together forever.

Her confidence faltered as she waded into the crowds near the besieged 7-Eleven store. It was near the gaudy lights of the fast-food chains on the edge of "the gap," a small, middle-class neighborhood on the South Side. People milled everywhere; the atmosphere crackled with a tension and a curiosity Maureen found somewhat morbid. It was so cold she couldn't understand why so many people were out on the street. But it was grim drama, one of life and death. Old women huddled into their worn winter coats and their eyes reflected concern for the hostages, the

177

police. Shivering young men nodded to each other, giving odds on the results of the night. "That sucker cop is a dead man, man," one predicted, the stranger's words cutting straight to Maureen's heart.

Maureen shuffled and edged as smoothly as she could through the crowd until she reached the police blockade, where gawkers packed tightly around a cluster of crying women. Television cameras were panning the crowd and reporters were pushing their way through the group as word filtered back that the two released girls were okay. Maureen caught glimpses of three generations of women, tears splashing down their faces, falling into the wrinkled furrows of the grandmother cheeks and tumbling onto the mahogany skin of a teenage girl while a dark-haired mother checked to see if her daughter was really all right. The three women clung to one another, their world restored, while the second family celebrated only a few feet away. Maureen was so happy for them, but, still, terror gripped her heart because that meant Tony was alone now. A dead man, isn't that what the stranger had predicted?

Maureen singled-mindedly pushed her way to the rope barricade. Taking advantage of the distracted officers, she slipped under its confines, walking toward the deceptively calm darkened store with only the jagged glass of the front windows hinting at the trouble within.

"Stop! Get back! You aren't allowed in here." A strong hand grabbed her arm. She stopped involuntarily, but never took her eyes from the store. The flipping red lights of the police cars projected an unnecessary sense of urgency as the frantic beams bounced off faces and the bullet-riddled storefront. Seeing it even from this distance gave it a spine-locking clarity. She'd been watching the news coverage, but it wasn't as discriminating as the naked eye. Trembling inside and saying another prayer, she wrenched her arm from the grasp.

"Lady, you've gotta stay behind the barrier." A man stood directly in her way, not a man, a policeman, his light blue helmet reflecting the flashing lights. She froze, staring at him. She didn't care if an army of them tried to hold her back.

"You don't understand; I've got to see him," she said breathlessly, pushing toward the storefront.

"Lady!" She struggled with the man and then jerked back, releasing his hold and outflanking him, running toward the storefront. "Lady! Stop! Lieutenant O'Connor!"

"Hold it. Hold it!" Other arms stopped her.

"Let me go! I've got to talk to him," she cried, pushing against his chest and twisting her body, her braid tumbling from under her open coat, her arms flying up to break his grip on her upper arms. "I've got to see him," she breathed, planning her maneuver. She feigned going in one direction with her eyes and shoulders, then quickly dodged the other way, escaping his reach.

"Hold it. Hold it!" he said, grabbing her from behind around her slender middle and lifting her from the ground. "Tell me what you want," he grunted. "Maybe I can help you."

"Let me go!" She wriggled and kicked, never taking her seeking eyes from the store.

"I don't want to hurt you!" he threatened her.

"He can't be all alone in there. Let me go!" she gasped, twisting her body out of his grasp the moment she had footing. "I've got to go to Tony. . . ." She pushed the officer away, swinging wildly at him like a punchy boxer, not really landing any blows. "Don't try to stop me!"

"It's all over with, lady," he shouted, warding off her blows. "It's all over."

"My God! Tony?" She stopped dead still.

"Captain DiRocco?" he asked, staring down into her bleak, pale face. "He's fine! He's fine! I'll take you to him. You can talk to him. Okay?"

"He's all right? You're sure?" The fighting and fear made her weak, and tears blurred the policeman's face.

"Yeah," he said, taking her arm firmly and guiding her toward the police cars. "No one unauthorized is allowed inside the perimeter, but I think the captain will make an exception for you."

As they snaked around the police and emergency vehicles, including Tony's gold Dodge parked helter-skelter in the cordoned-off street, she saw him. He was standing in a circle of reporters, but she caught snatches of his frame, his dark hair, his hands jammed into the pockets of his coat, only escaping for brief moments to emphasize a point or two. He was huddled into

179

his tan trench coat. It was the first time she had ever seen him cold, she realized as she canvassed him for other differences or injuries, not able to take her eyes off him. She wanted him. But here, on this foreign territory, he seemed so different. In the harsh lights his stony profile looked stern, determined, hard. She remembered his words about tough, smart cops.

"You better hold up here just a minute so you don't get into the media thing," Lieutenant O'Connor told her. "I'll say one thing, lady. Captain DiRocco is a very lucky man." He smiled at her before he moved closer to his superior.

She closed her eyes, listening to the strained sound of his familiar voice. She longed to hear it gentle and mellow.

". . . To save the victims," Tony said to the reporters as her eyes feasted upon him once more. He was safe. He was a cop, in a good-guy-bad-guy world, he was safe.

"Isn't that a naive Pollyanna attitude for the Chicago police department, Captain?" a cynical reporter asked.

"That's our job—to serve and protect," Tony reminded him.

"But how much can you really do?"

He hesitated, clearing his throat. Maureen smiled. He was the man she loved. He was her brave knight that charged into her life, turning it into a wonderful once-upon-a-time. She loved him. ". . . All efforts should be made to save innocent victims of crime, whether they be store owners, hostages, or whoever. So in my district, within the bounds of the law, good police procedure, and officer safety, that's what we'll strive for. Sometimes we'll be successful and sometimes we won't. We were fortunate tonight."

His distinct dark hair and features gave him a starkly handsome and confident air despite his hard professional mask. She lusted to see a soft warm light in his eyes.

". . . About officer safety?" Another reporter spoke up. "You let yourself wide open in there—"

"That's all the questions right now," Tony interrupted. "I'll have a prepared statement for you in the morning," he said firmly as he signaled other uniformed officers to urge the reporters away.

"Thanks, DiRocco."

"In the morning . . ."

"You came charging through again, kid."

"Thanks, Mike." Tony nodded to the streetwise newsman. As the flock of reporters broke up, Maureen retreated and ducked around the corner, leaning against the back doors of a black and white SWAT truck for support. What if he didn't want to be a part of her fairy tale? He had a whole week to think also. What if he didn't want her? What if . . .

"Tony, a couple more things." Lieutenant Jonathan O'Connor interrupted him, shielding Maureen from his line of sight, waiting until they were alone before he continued.

"Yeah, Jon." Tony was bone-tired and knew only one voice, one smile could set him right tonight.

"There's seven very lucky people that owe you everything, Tony." O'Connor clapped a hand on his shoulder. Tony respected Jon; they'd worked well together, yet they'd talked only about business, the job. He wondered why, feeling tired and vulnerable to everyone. It was loving Maureen that exposed him to people, and she didn't come. Now he wished he were untouchable again.

"God, I feel old," Tony sighed, shrugging deeper into his coat and looking up into the hazy red night, steam from his mouth rising up to join the breath of the city—his city. "Someone told me I could argue with the devil and win." Tony laughed. "I think I did today." He looked at the other burly cop. "I talked that sucker to death. I lied, I made up things, and even remembered old stories my father and grandfather told me. I said anything just to keep those two little girls alive. I wore him right down." Tony breathed deeply. "But that's not the argument I needed to win." He shook his head. "You know what I mean?"

"Yeah." Jon smiled at him. "I'll do the reports. Go home and rest. Or whatever." Jon O'Connor smirked.

"Yeah, home." Tony hadn't been back to the apartment for a week. He couldn't live there and not have Maureen, but he couldn't live away either. The week seemed like an eternity. He'd tasted her velvet skin and made love with her through the night. But one night wasn't nearly enough. Not even close. He needed to be with her now, always. He'd said she had to come to him, had to reach her own decision, and he was bitter and hurt by her delay. But after not knowing whether he would live through the day, things became abundantly clear. He wanted her to be part

181

of his life and he refused to take less. He would swallow his pride and go to her, talk to her, make her understand. He needed her warm, accepting center, her arms cradling and coddling, loving him. He wondered if she even knew about this stand-off today. It started off being just a Saturday morning; she could be anywhere. For hours he wanted to tell her how much he loved her and how he laid down his gun to help others. How he loved her for knowing that about him before he did.

"Tony, there's one other matter for you to handle," Jon O'-Connor started to say. "There's a civilian—a woman—a good-looking blonde, who fought her way past our crowd control." Tony struggled to keep excitement from his expression. "Anyway, she insisted that she see you about something."

"Where is she?" Tony asked, his hope rising.

"She was just here," Jon said curiously, looking over his shoulder. He called out, walking to the rear of the police van, Tony following. "Miss?" He found her bracing herself against the back of the truck. "Miss, here's Captain DiRocco."

"Thank you," she started to say but only a whisper came out as she caught Tony's sparkling eyes. He studied her, memorized her, hungrily scanning her face and frame. He had thought about her day and night for a week. And she stood tentatively watching him, as though she would bolt away at any moment.

"Are you all right?" Maureen asked finally.

"Yes." He wanted to hold her in his arms so badly his body trembled inside from the need, but he stubbornly stood firm, protecting and depriving himself of the pleasure. He couldn't stand to hold her again if he wouldn't get to keep her forever. "You shouldn't have come to the South Side. It's dangerous," he said flatly.

"Dangerous!" She wrung her hands. He'd fantasized that when she saw him, she would throw herself into his arms and beg him to love her and stay with her always. His dreams crumbled, and they both stood tensely still.

"Lieutenant O'Connor said you had something important to tell me." Tony gestured to his colleague, who was already walking away.

"Yes."

"So tell me." He refused to give an inch. He'd been arguing

and driving hard bargains for hours. But now that he was nego-
tiating for his own life and happiness, compromise was impossible. He stood like rock. He would let her try to get rid of him.
He was ready to fight and win. He always got whom he was
after—always.

"I . . . ummm . . . I was afraid I wouldn't get to tell you. Are
you really all right?"

"Yeah." He breathed out, looking out over the crowds behind
the sawhorses and ropes, the police light washing over the faces,
flipping in a haunting red tide. He looked back at Maureen and
saw the fear in her face, wanting to embrace her and tell her it
was all right. She didn't belong even close to his work. "You look
really terrific." His eyes locked on her and lovingly caressed her.
"Especially for someone who just fought her way through a
police barricade. You know I could run you in for that?"

"But you'd never let me go."

"Never." He agreed quietly. Maureen smoothed back her hair
with her shaking hand and gave him a small smile.

"You look like you need a shave," she whispered as her fingers
scraped over his stubbly jaw that tensed from her light caress.
She cupped his face between her hands that cruised down the
column of his throat. She could touch him, feel he was well and
safe, his dark eyes devouring her.

"Yeah." He lifted her chin with two fingers and tipped his
head to the side. "You have your hair in a braid again."

"Yes."

"Are you going to take the braid out before you go to bed?"
he asked, breathing faster. The pleasant reedy notes of his voice
drew her closer as her regard caressed his cheeks and jaw.

"Yes," she whispered, leaning her hips gently into him and
circling her arms around his neck. He swallowed hard and
grabbed her arms as he held her away from his tightly coiled
body.

"Don't, Maureen," he rasped into the cold air, the cloud of
their breath filling the red night sky.

"What?"

"Tell me!" he commanded.

"I, ah, I was afraid . . ." He released her arms and reeled away
from her. Neither spoke. "How does it feel to have rescued seven

183

people today?" she began again. She smiled briefly with pride, but he still didn't look at her. "Does that help make up for Cluny?"

"Nothing can make up for him," he said, turning his heated gaze on her, starting at the first button of her coat and moving up to her quivering pink lips. She couldn't stem the cold chill of isolation that had frozen her for days. His loving embrace was the only thing that could warm her. "But it helps." He nodded, flipping his trench coat and jacket open to jam a nervous hand into the pocket of his slacks. She craved his heat.

"They were all lucky to have you there."

"Yeah. I'm a great guy," he muttered sarcastically. He ventured another look at her lips, her cheeks, her dark lake-blue eyes that suddenly avoided his.

"The truth is you could have been killed, masked crusader, champion of truth and justice." She tried to tease him, but nearly choked on the words.

"What's the real truth, princess?"

"I won't lie to you, Captain. I don't want you in danger again." He exhaled his frustration in a billowy cloud. He didn't want to hear the same old story. "I've had too long to think—too long without you. You could've been killed today. I don't know what to do about that. I'll always worry about you and say prayers for you." She stepped over to him, her hand brushing his cheek. "I know only one very basic truth. I—I love you very much. I may be afraid . . . but I love you. I need to be with you so you can be brave for both of us."

"For how long?" he asked relentlessly. He'd known for weeks that she loved him, but it was unbearably sweet to hear her say the words. "How long will you love me?"

"Forever." She smiled.

"Will you be my wife?" he painstakingly enunciated each word as she inched closer and he looked down at her upturned face.

"Yes." She listed toward him, drawn by his warmth. He kissed her tenderly and thoroughly, holding her close, as if he'd never let go.

"It took our love to slay a dragon, princess, but now you're mine," he said, gathering her up into his arms. "I need you," he said, kissing her, allowing her feet to touch the ground as his kiss deepened.

"I love you." She wound grateful arms around his neck, swaying her hips gently forward to meet his. She allowed herself to look deep into his melancholy eyes, and she could see the future clearly now, no clouds or haze, no fear or guilt, only love. "I love you," she murmured, kissing and nuzzling his neck. It seemed so blissfully easy to say now. "I love you," she repeated over and over.

"That's all I'll ever ask from you," he whispered against her hot rosy cheek, enveloping his princess in a passionate embrace of completion, tenderly seeking her pink lips for a confirming caress, promising many glorious nights ahead.

"Tony? We're about wrapped up here." Lieutenant O'Connor surprised them, splitting their embrace as he strided around the corner of the truck.

"Yeah, sure, Jon," Tony said, not quite able to take his gaze from Maureen.

"I'll handle the paperwork, Captain," he said, waiting for Tony's reply.

"Thank you, Lieutenant O'Connor," Maureen said graciously, giving him a wonderful smile, then added, putting her arm possessively through Tony's, "I'm going to take my future husband home now and put him to bed."

"Ah . . . yes, ma'am!" Jon grinned, lowering his head. "Ah, congratulations. Tony said he was going to find you and ask you to marry him. I'm glad you said yes."

"Yeah, thanks, Jon," Tony said quickly, not meeting the lieutenant's eye and intentionally missing Maureen's raised brow. "I'll see you tomorrow." The police lieutenant smiled and nodded before leaving the couple alone again.

"You're blushing, Captain," Maureen pointed out, pursing her pink lips and continuing to study Tony.

"I'm not blushing!" he insisted irritably, putting an arm around her and guiding her toward his car. "I used up all my blushes a long time ago."

"Hmmm!" She tipped her head to the side and unabashedly scanned him, relishing the ruddy tint to his cheeks. "I'm under

Nicki's strict orders to get 'that grouchy old cop home where he belongs.' "

"Old!" He laughed, hugging her closer to him as they walked. "Doesn't that kid know my life is just beginning? I'll have to talk to her."

"She's staying with Myron," Maureen started. "So we'll have the house to ourselves for a while. So we could be alone together and . . . ummm . . . you know." He opened the car door for her but held her arm to delay her from moving away from him.

"No, tell me," he taunted her, doing his best to be serious.

"Let's go home, my brave knight," she whispered, "and I'll show you."

Candlelight Ecstasy Romances™

Candlelight Ecstasy Romances™

$1.95 each

CANDLELIGHT
Ecstasy Supreme